Donald. G. Ciesielski
Central Lutheran
Theological Seminary
Fremont, Nebraska

April 6, 1960

MAN *and* WIFE

A SOURCE BOOK OF

Family Attitudes,
Sexual Behavior
and Marriage Counseling

MAN *and* WIFE

A SOURCE BOOK OF
Family Attitudes, Sexual Behavior and Marriage Counseling

Edited by

EMILY HARTSHORNE MUDD, M.S.W., Ph.D.

PROFESSOR OF FAMILY STUDY, DEPARTMENT OF PSYCHIATRY
SCHOOL OF MEDICINE, UNIVERSITY OF PENNSYLVANIA
AND DIRECTOR, MARRIAGE COUNCIL OF PHILADELPHIA

and ARON KRICH, Ed.D.

W · W · NORTON & COMPANY · INC · *New York*

To Those Who Are Pioneering
in Collaboration between the
Medical and Social Sciences

Contents

Part One   The Making and Breaking of Marriage

Contents

Contributors

KENNETH E. APPEL, M.D., *Professor and Chairman, Department of Psychiatry, School of Medicine, University of Pennsylvania*

EMILY HARTSHORNE MUDD, Ph.D., *Professor of Family Study in Psychiatry and Director, Division of Family Study, Department of Psychiatry, School of Medicine, University of Pennsylvania; Director, Marriage Council of Philadelphia*

LEON J. SAUL, M.D., *Professor of Clinical Psychiatry, School of Medicine, University of Pennsylvania*

PHILIP Q. ROCHE, M.D., *Assistant Professor of Psychiatry, School of Medicine, University of Pennsylvania*

FREDERICK H. ALLEN, M.D., *Professor of Psychiatry, Emeritus, School of Medicine, University of Pennsylvania; Former Director, Philadelphia Child Guidance Clinic; Consulting Psychiatrist, Philadelphia Board of Education*

M. ROYDEN C. ASTLEY, M.D., *Former Assistant Professor of Psychiatry, School of Medicine, University of Pennsylvania; Professor of Psychiatry, School of Medicine, University of Pittsburgh*

JAMES H. S. BOSSARD, A.M., Ph.D., L.H.D., *Professor of Sociology, William T. Carter Professor of Child Development, and Professor of Sociology in Psychiatry, School of Medicine, University of Pennsylvania*

MARTIN G. GOLDBERG, M.D., *Instructor in Psychiatry, School of Medicine, University of Pennsylvania*

NOCHEM S. WINNET, *Former Judge of the Municipal Court, Philadelphia, Pa.*

EDWIN E. AUBREY, B.D., Ph.D., *Former Professor of Religious Thought, University of Pennsylvania*

A. H. CLEMENS, Ph.D., *Assistant Professor of Sociology and Director, Marriage Counseling Center, The Catholic University of America, Washington, D. C.*

RABBI DAVID H. WICE, M.A., D.D., D.H.L., *Rodeph Sholam Synagogue, Philadelphia, Pa.*

xi

WILLIAM L. PELTZ, M.D., *Assistant Professor of Psychiatry, School of Medicine, University of Pennsylvania*

WILLIAM V. FITTIPOLDI, M.D., *Former Associate in Psychiatry, School of Medicine, University of Pennsylvania*

PAUL O. KLINGENSMITH, M.D., *Associate Professor of Obstetrics and Gynecology, School of Medicine, University of Pennsylvania*

O. SPURGEON ENGLISH, M.D., *Professor of Psychiatry, Temple University Medical School and Hospital; Former member Medical Supervisory Committee, Marriage Council of Philadelphia*

ARON KRICH, Ed. D., *Grant Foundation Fellow, Marriage Council of Philadelphia*

Foreword

"It is difficult if not impossible for most people to think otherwise than in the fashion of their own period."

—George Bernard Shaw.

THE extraordinary scientific developments of the past century are changing the patterns of human life at speeds never approached before in recorded history. In the medical world, the solid bedrock of knowledge resulting from research in the basic sciences has necessitated revolutionary changes in both medical education and practice. One of these changes that is proving most invigorating and successful is that from the very beginning the medical student is brought into the laboratory as an active participant. Subsequently, he is given an opportunity to assist in the application of the scientific principles so learned to the care of patients. The laboratory has thus inevitably become the anteroom to the ward, and the rewards are manifest in the saving of lives of the sick and injured.

However, the physician of today should not feel complacent, for he is confronted by an expanding field of failure in which, so far, the laboratory is of scant assistance. Just as the use of an expressway results in a number of accidents, the very speed with which scientific discovery has revolutionized life may be a factor in the vast increase in those ailments generally associated with stress—alcoholism, drug addiction, juvenile delinquency, rising divorce rates, psychosomatic illness, even psychosis itself. Physicians are already obliged to deal with these conditions which, as the obvious physical illnesses come more and more under control, will undoubtedly represent a greatly increased percentage of the practice of tomorrow. Physicians engaged in general or family practice, internal medicine, pediatrics, and psychiatry will be the first to experience this change and should therefore be prepared to cope with the problems of psychosocial health. What, then, should the medical student be taught now about these human problems for which the laboratory has as yet no precise diagnostic tests, for which there are as yet no specific remedies? Because these are lacking, should he be left to cope with these problems of daily life for the first time in practice, to learn how to handle them the old hard slow way by trial and error, by the accumulation of mistakes not so obvious and dramatic perhaps as similar scientific errors, but just as real, just as damaging?

For some years we have tried ways and means of arousing an awareness of psychosocial problems at the very time when the student is being steeped in laboratory methods. Perhaps such problems can never be solved by what we now consider scientific methods; but surely we should try to bring to bear on them the same interest, the same attitude of mind that has produced such rewards in other fields of medicine. This will not be accomplished by studious avoidance in the medical-school course.

It was in this setting that two of the authors of this book, Dr. Kenneth Appel and Dr. Emily Mudd, first suggested the inauguration of a course in Family Attitudes and Sexual Behavior for senior medical students. Perhaps because we were unable to think other than in the fashion of scientific medical education of the day, it was offered as an elective to be taken outside of regular class hours. Its success is evidenced by the attendance and interest of students under these conditions.

The book to which this brief message serves as a foreword deals with a segment of life that is of real importance in the promotion or impairment of both physical and mental health: the relationships between man and wife. This is an area into which the physician must enter in his daily practice, an area in which his greatest skill in human relations is often needed. It is our hope that the book will open new channels from which may flow a better understanding of the problems that will be encountered, and through which may be returned some of the effort that has been so fruitful in other fields of medicine. For it is our belief that this side of medical education can be fostered without neglecting the other; that tact, no less than fact, can be learned.

JOHN McK. MITCHELL, M.D.
Dean, School of Medicine
University of Pennsylvania

Introduction

BY KENNETH E. APPEL, M.D.

LIVING involves activity, contacts, and social relationships. Life can be courageous and zestful, or be unhappy and full of suffering. Relationships between people can be creative and stimulating, or be frustrating, paralyzing, destructive. People can be friendly and co-operative, or antagonistic, distrustful, and withdrawn.

Medicine is becoming increasingly aware of the importance of the above relationships for the health of the individual. New horizons have been developed since the days of Virchow, Pasteur, and Koch. Biological medicine has been extended beyond the basic, elementary concepts of cells, infectious organisms, and immunity by the researches of Pavlov, Cannon, and Selye. Their studies have contributed to modern medicine, not only in deepening the understanding of the physiology and chemistry of the organism, but in emphasizing the importance of environmental and social relationships with other organisms. It is chiefly through contacts with other human beings that fear, frustration, anger, and pain enter the picture. Freud made microscopic analyses of the formative experiences of early life in the family. Wolf and Wolff have shown the influence of culture and social relationships on physiology. Talking to someone may change the temperature of the body many degrees, or may change the circulation and physiological equilibrium, and may thus determine disease or health.

New concepts have appeared in medicine: stress diseases, psychosomatic medicine, psychological medicine, psycho-social medicine. Medicine is no longer simply a biological science; it has significant and inescapable social and economic ramifications whether with regard to etiology, treatment, cure, or prevention. The educational aspect of medicine, that is, social education which is of great importance for prevention, has barely been recognized.

Early home experiences guide, misguide, or distort the normal basic impulses, and influence their development into constructive, creative social living or the reverse. They pave the way for co-operative living or for rebellious, destructive attitudes and relationships. Early home life also forms the cultural sources for the behavior patterns of future generations; their health, their disease, and their possibilities for survival. Attitudes toward others and to the basic impulses of love and sex—whether the individual finds these impulses satisfying and creative, or full of guilt and shame, incapacitating, paralyzing—are determined in great measure in childhood.

The course in family attitudes, sexual behavior, and marriage counseling, on which this book is based has made important contributions to medical education by widening the horizons of understanding and by offering new tools of treatment and prevention. This course was initiated and organized by the Family Study Division of the Department of Psychiatry of the University of Pennsylvania, and was made possible through the encouragement and co-operation of Dean John Mitchell of the School of Medicine.

This book presents not only the contents of the lectures, but the philosophy of the course. It offers new frames of reference for the practice of medicine. A distinctive feature is its relation to religion and law. Three lectures are given, each by an appropriate spokesman, on the attitudes towards sex, marriage, family life, and divorce of Roman Catholicism, Protestantism, and Judaism. One lecture is given by an expert in family law. It is important for medical students and young practitioners to understand the customs and values of families of different religious faiths, and the implications of these values for medical treatment. As it is, some important decisions involving religious and legal matters are left to the chance acquisition of miscellaneous experience. This course has been eminently successful as attested by the recognition it has received. This book shares with the public new aspects of medicine; new opportunities for understanding, for treatment, and for the alleviation and prevention of suffering.

Preface

THE purpose of this book is to make available to professional persons working intimately with people, and to the intelligent layman who as husband, wife, or parent is personally involved in close human relationships, material which has proved itself to be informative, stimulating, and practically useful in understanding and helping people with their development and their problems. This material is focused on marriage and family life in the contemporary United States. The emphasis is on what can be done by the everyday citizen himself, or by him with the help of a professional person, to achieve greater competence in his intimate interpersonal relations, and to resolve problems when these are encountered.

Among the many excellent volumes now available on health, human relationships, and marriage this book is unique in two respects. First, because it grew out of a five-year experiment in communicating information and attitudes on marriage and family living of functional usefulness to intelligent young people, namely senior medical students. Secondly, because as a symposium it contains summarized contributions from many of the foremost authorities in this field, not as isolated chapters, but as part of a unified whole to which each author was closely committed through creative planning and through participation in teaching in the course. In addition all but two of the authors have had an integral part in the functioning of the Philadelphia Marriage Council, the third such service in the United States, and through this have had first-hand experience in working with troubled marriages.

For the convenience of the reader the volume is divided into four parts: the making and breaking of marriage, the moral climate of marriage, mating and mismating, and the meaning and process of counseling. Thus, should the reader wish an over-all view, by following the text from beginning to end he may achieve perspective and insight on the difficulties people are actually having in marriage; the relation of these complications to the individuals' early conditions of growth; the interaction of their difficulties with the salient features of their environments; the impact and reflection of early conditioning in the vital area of sex; and finally, something of what can be done to modify or eliminate these painful and destructive situations. Or should the reader prefer to explore some specific area, the chapter headings will lead him to his choice. The Appendix contains a list of books and pamphlets found by marriage counselors and their clients to be helpful in preparation for or adjustment to marriage, and also a list of national organizations from which information may be obtained concerning reliable sources of help in local communities.

The book thus lends itself to serving as a broadly informative text in functional courses on marital problems and marriage counseling for medical students, for divinity students, for clinical psychologists, for social workers, for teachers, for nurses, for lawyers, and for other related professional groups. It also offers the intelligent layman a combination not now available of background information, perspective, and practical assistance.

Work was undertaken for this symposium with the full recognition that the innate complexities of the psychic attributes of the human organism have been subjected to only the early stages of rigorous scientific scrutiny. The authors accept the fact that there are varying conceptualizations of personality and its interactions, varying philosophies concerning how the person coming for help may most adequately be assisted, and varying criteria of how professional persons can be trained adequately and accredited to offer reliable services in marital preparation and problems. They are familiar with the efforts of professional groups, notably the American Association of Marriage Counselors, organized in 1946, to formalize and maintain minimum standards for workers in marriage education and counseling.*

Marriage counseling is here defined as the process through which a professionally trained counselor assists two people (the engaged or married partners) to develop abilities in resolving to some workable degree the problems that trouble them in their interpersonal relationships as they move into a marriage, live with it, or (in a small number of instances) move out of it. The focus of the counselor's approach is considered to be the relationship between the two people in the marriage rather than, as in psychiatric therapy, the reorganization of the personality structure of the individual. The theoretical framework behind this approach presents the following hypothesis: if an individual can experience, during the counseling process, new understanding of himself and his marriage partner, and more satisfying ways of using himself in his daily relationships in marriage and with his famly, he should be able to apply these acquired abilities to other problem situations as these may arise in his daily living.

This point of view and procedure was developed at the Marriage Council of Philadelphia, established in 1932 as the third such service in the United States. This agency has always been nonprofit, available to anyone, regardless of race, creed, or national origin, and sponsored by men and women of recognizedly high professional caliber. It has always employed professionally trained staff as counselors, primarily social workers, with part-time consulting psychiatrists. It is supported by fees from counseling with individuals and groups, by family-life education, by

* 1956 Membership in this association consisted of 19 per cent physicians (of whom 5 per cent were psychiatrists), 16 per cent educators, 20 per cent social workers, 14 per cent clinical psychologists, 12 per cent sociologists, 15 per cent ministers, 4 per cent lawyers. Some of these members use marriage counseling skills within their private practice, others in hospital clinics, social agencies, churches, university counseling services, or agencies organized specifically for marriage counseling. The Association has prepared a *Casebook in Marriage Counseling*, in press, 1957, with Association Press, New York.

grants from private foundations, by state and federal funds for training and research, and by membership contributions from interested citizens in the community. Several hundred such organizations in the United States offer marriage counseling in urban areas under differing auspices. All are operated without financial profit, the majority charging nominal fees based on individual income and payable to the agency. In a group of cases from the Marriage Council in which both clients and their partners were counseled, a study under funds from the United States Public Health Service found that approximately "5 per cent of the cases showed retrogression, from 25 to 30 per cent showed no movement (improvement) at all, and from 60 to 65 per cent showed positive movement (or improvement)." *

In 1952 the Marriage Council was affiliated officially with the School of Medicine, University of Pennsylvania, and became the operational unit of a new Division of Family Study, Department of Psychiatry. It was following this affiliation that the course in Family Attitudes, Sexual Behavior, and Marriage Counseling was initiated.

A venture with different contributors can sink or swim on the basis of the *esprit de corps* established among the authors, the editors, and the publishers. It would be presumptuous for the editors to thank the contributors. Without them there would be no book, and without the vision and courage of the Chairman of the Department of Psychiatry, Dr. Kenneth E. Appel, and the generous appropriation received for this purpose from The Grant Foundation of New York City, there would have been no course on which to base a book. If appreciation is to be expressed, it rightfully belongs to the potentials of education as a means for improving the lot of mankind. Due to a belief in these potentials this group of professionally experienced men and women were

* "Factors Affecting Movement in Casework," Malcolm G. Preston, Emily H. Mudd, Hazel B. Froscher, *Social Casework*, March, 1953, Vol. 34, pp. 103–111.

willing to dedicate their time and effort to teaching the art and science of family relations and subsequently to writing this book. With a spirit of hopefulness they have assigned their royalties to the work of the Division of Family Study.

In the passage of time during the preparation of this manuscript two of our contributors have died. To the great sorrow of his friends and associates, Professor Edwin E. Aubrey passed away quite unexpectedly in September, 1956. His loss will be felt keenly by the University and by the students, who considered him one of their most popular and respected teachers. Dr. William V. Fittipoldi died suddenly in 1953. He was an enthusiastic and helpful participant in the planning and execution of the first two years of teaching the Family Attitudes, Sexual Behavior, and Marriage Counseling course. His loss is felt deeply by his professional associates, his students, and his patients.

There are a few associates to whom we wish personally to express our appreciation and gratitude. Among these in particular are the Staff Members of the Division of Family Study who, by their willingness to substitute for the Director, made available to her the necessary measure of free time to pursue this work. To Dr. Stuart Mudd, who audited the first year's course and read the early drafts of the manuscript, we owe a special debt. From his vantage point as a natural scientist and a husband he was an unfailing source of enthusiasm and often-needed encouragement. Acknowledgment is made also to the careful secretarial assistance of Mrs. Clara Lexey, Mrs. Elizabeth Milligan, and Mrs. Gertrude Payne, each of whom participated with interest in the preparation of the manuscript.

This has been a unique experience in communication and co-operation with an extended family group. It included the honeymoon phase, the settling-down period, and living with stress. As it approaches the tranquility of accomplishment, we can report with exhilaration that at no point was there a break in the mutual feelings of support, co-operation, and friendliness. Much of the optimism herein reflected was made possible by the good fortune of finding Dr. Aron Krich willing to associate his skill and imaginative persistence as co-editor. For this editor this period truly enhances the continuing belief in the creative strength of human relationships.

EMILY H. MUDD

Part One

The Making and Breaking
of Marriage

———————

Chapter 1

Problems with Which People Want
Help in Sex and Marriage

KENNETH E. APPEL, M.D.

ACH individual invests life with feelings that make it tolerable and zestful or unhappy and intolerable. These feelings are in part determined by early experiences in the family. The satisfaction, happiness, and wisdom of the husband and wife determine to an appreciable extent whether their children will enter into society and contribute, or whether they will represent dissident and destructive forces. When two people marry, there ensues an interaction of their needs, habits, and personality tendencies that can be growth-producing or that can, unfortunately, produce difficulty and maladjustment for one or both partners.

The chapters that follow present a number of situations of conflict in people as husbands, wives, or parents. Basically, of course, problems in personal and family living involve some conflict of attitudes, expectations, beliefs, prejudices, and fears. In a personal problem, the conflict is between differing attitudes *within* the individual or, frequently, between the individual's attitudes, desires, and aspirations and the mores of his culture and society. In family problems there is the additional possibility of conflict between the attitudes, beliefs, and aspirations of one family member and those of another member. In such situations the individual is the center of many competing forces and drives. When these conflicts are unrecognized or unresolved, the price may be great unhappiness accompanied often by physical and emotional ill health.

The origin of my own interest in marriage counseling was my discovery of the extent to which marital maladjustment appeared in patients, masquerading or expressing itself unconsciously in unhappiness, vocational ineffectiveness, alcoholism, psychosomatic symptoms, nervous illness, mental disease, and even suicide. Let me indicate to you the almost unbelievable array of such problems with a sampling of actual situations drawn from a few days of my office practice. Although these cases represent extremes of abnormality and pathology, they illustrate what can happen when attempts at reeducation or counseling have not been sought, have been unavailable, or have failed at incipient stages of difficulty.

Here is a tremendously successful broker. He is masterful and dominating, and this is the basis on which he tries to live with his wife. She wants from him, instead of the thousands of dollars he showers upon her, a little warmth and affection. And these she does not get. She has colitis; has difficulty getting rid of him. They have been married and divorced four times, going through this performance every three or four years for sixteen years. They ask me: "How can you bring us together?"

Here is a girl who wants to marry, to be normal. She has a beautiful body and noticeably attractive features. Three years ago a boy stimulated her genitally by hand. She was brought up in her own estimation as "a blue blood," and her tradition taught that nice boys would not take such liberties with girls. She became hallucinated, delusional. Her family's domination, their outlook on the world, had never given the girl an opportunity to learn what life was about. She had a schizophrenic breakdown. Now she is just a shell of beauty with the cultural urge to marry.

Here is a scientist, a brilliant man, forty-five years old. He is a perfectionist, a martinet. He has a paranoid wife who married him on the rebound. She continually accuses him of having affairs with other women. Their life is a battle of wills in which he becomes either aggressive or neurotic for a number of weeks or months while she becomes either tolerant of an unhappy home situation or goes markedly paranoid. That has been their history for over twenty-five years of marriage.

Here is an engineer who was an honor student at his university. He was an only boy brought up with several sisters. He married a girl who was brought up with five brothers. She complains that he is not competitive enough, does not go out and get good jobs. There is premature ejaculation, little sexual satisfaction, and the act is becoming more and more infrequent. He is a passive man whose aggressive wife is taunting him, castrating him intellectually, saying: "You are not a man. I don't think life is worth living with you."

Here is a sixty-five-year-old professional man who deals with his love life by pinching his wife or kicking her *derrière*. In his childhood someone pervertly stimulated him. He does not treat women well, and yet he deals with many women in his work. He can only be understood in terms of the hostility and tensions under which he is living.

Here is a man with depression. He is in his forties, married, has chronic indigestion, and is almost completely impotent. His father died young, and he supported four sisters and a mother to whom he was devoted. Life was so serious and he and his mother were so pressed financially that he had not much chance for affection and warmth. He likes his wife's companionship but does not like the intimacies of bodies. He is unconsciously homosexual and worried about the situation. Neither he nor his wife will get a divorce, because both are devout Catholics who believe that they must carry on with their life as it is.

Here is a college girl whose mother was a suicide when she

was five. She was a tomboy. Now she fears homosexuality. She has multiple pains, many anatomic disturbances, palpitations, and cardiac and upper gastrointestinal distress. Her trouble is frustration of her security and love impulses.

Here is a woman who has had a hysterectomy, a mastectomy, a thrombectomy, a nephrectomy, and before these many childhood diseases. How adequate a sexual partner could she be? Her husband, who has never been seriously ill, has normal sex impulses.

Here is a successful artist married to a research man. This was a lonely boy who hated his dominating meticulous, obsessive mother. He married a vital, warm, lovely, fleshy girl who overflows with love. There is hardly any sex. And so she has drifted toward a relationship with someone else. This marriage is ending in divorce.

Now here is a very successful, aggressive, self-made industrialist who married his childhood sweetheart. She is a combination of doll and mother, and has always been frigid. For quite a few years the husband has moved into extramarital satisfactions. He is becoming depressed, thinks it might be wrong. He says: "Doctor, don't give me any sedative to cut down my sexual function. That's not the way I want you to help me." He is not sure, nor am I, how he does want me to help him.

Here is a prominent member of the community who, because of his frustrations, is tremendously preoccupied with his bowels. It is amazing the amount of time he spends worrying about this specific function, which has become a substitute for a satisfactory love life. As happens so often, areas of physiology and anatomy are substituted for instinctual frustrations.

I could fill pages with tragic examples that represent only a few days of one psychiatrist's practice. Hate, fear, disillusionment, and destruction of the self and others extend into the family and the community. Here is a picture of pathology, of life as it sometimes is. We have touched kaleidoscopically on the forces that motivate people in their behavior. It is obvious that these are not just problems of sexology or biology. These vignettes of severe conflict and maladjustment could be thought of as a kind of prologue to the more extended examination offered by the various specialists contributing to this source book. Culture, tradition, ideals, religion, all have relevance to the problems with which people must grapple. Because of these multiple dimensions we attempt in this book to present a broad understanding of the varieties of tensions and conflicts that people in trouble may have. All the contributors are concerned with either the intrinsic needs and psychological motivations of the individual or with the demands made upon him by his culture.

As one describes people's needs and motivations, the implication is often made that these patterns of behavior are pathological per se. Thus it is easy to talk of a man's need to be mothered, or of his need to dominate, or of his need to escape from reality. But none of these needs are necessarily pathological, and many very worthwhile, emotionally healthy people have such needs. Similarly, in examining two people who are "in love" with each other, we may observe that *he* wants to be mastered while *she* likes to dominate people. That does not necessarily mean that these two people will not be able to have a very fine relationship. We must consider the interaction of people's needs and how they satisfy or fail to satisfy each other.

It is not for us to take a holier-than-thou attitude and overtly or subtly condemn such interactions in religious, psychiatric, or psychoanalytic terms. It is essential that in all our relationships we recognize the feelings and biases that each of us has. Rather than pretend to a superhuman degree of personal maturity and objectivity in our relationships with people, it is most helpful if we can achieve the ability to look at ourselves a little, to know our weaknesses as well as our strengths. In doing this we can learn psychologically and, as Whittaker has put it, expand the "growing edge" of our own maturity.

Observations on the processes involved when one individual helps another have particular import for all who find themselves in a helping or person-serving role, and especially for the physician. All physicians see many cases where symptoms do not subside as they should under the usual methods of treatment, when convalescents do not convalesce, when recovery from accidents or surgical procedure is unusually protracted for no obvious reason or for no biophysical reason. Physicians are aware in these cases that somehow or other emotional factors must be entering into the condition. Yet their accustomed ways of treatment are often so definite, concrete, aggressive, and authoritarian that there is lacking the subtlety and finesse needed for dealing with psychological problems. Marriage problems are an inevitable part of the work that comes to every doctor's office, but physicians' efforts in this field are frequently self-defeating because their knowledge and skill are limited. There are, furthermore, patients who are unable to discuss intimate and personal problems with the physician because not all medical personnel have learned to put such patients at their ease. At the same time, many patients with marital problems who need expert help will not consult available psychiatrists because of the prevailing attitude that psychiatrists deal only with abnormal conditions, with mental disease.

Fortunately, there is an increasing group of workers with special knowledge and ability in dealing with problems of interpersonal relationships, especially in marriage and the family. Their work has helpfully supplemented that of the physician, as will be seen later in Dr. Mudd's discussion of some of the cases that come to the Marriage Council of Philadelphia, one of the earliest community clinics of this type which, in 1950, became the operational unit of a new Division of Family Study in the Department of Psychiatry of the University of Pennsylvania, School of Medicine. The cases described above illustrate types and variations of chronically deteriorated situations. The possibility of alleviating such situations at earlier and less acute periods of disturbance makes marriage counseling a community need.

Marriage counseling is sought by men and women, both before and after marriage. About one-third of the work at the Philadelphia Marriage Council is with couples or individuals who are single and considering marriage or who are already engaged. Premarital counseling plays a role in trying to help women and men evaluate their goals for marriage—their expectations, both defined and implied, vague or unconscious. It facilitates understanding of the balance of forces involved in love for the fiancé and in the vision of continued companionship. With women, it is important to explore their natural desire to be wives and mothers—their wish for the prestige of having a husband, and, possibly, the hope of being supported and having a comfortable home. With men, it may be helpful to evaluate the basis of any hesitancy about marrying and their feelings about the responsibilities of supporting a wife and family. It is worthwhile to encourage more of an interchange between the partners to make clear just what the girl expects from her husband and the man from his wife.

Postmaritally, the job of the counselor may be to help the wife evaluate whether she expected too much and is now seeing the marriage in terms that are blacker than they need be. The husband may be helped to figure out what his wife expects from him and whether he can meet these expectations more adequately than he is doing, what he hoped for from marriage, and how possible or real his ideas are in terms of his wife and job. And finally, the two can be assisted in getting together on what their respective roles should be.

In a detailed study of several hundred cases at the Marriage Council,[1] a very noticeable difference appeared between the

[1] This study was made (in part) under a research grant from the National Institutes of Health, Public Health Service.

premaritally and postmaritally counseled groups and in the number of problems presented. Of the postmarital clients, 56 per cent presented ten or more problems each, while only 20 per cent of the premarital clients presented this many. However, even in the simplest cases, there are usually several areas in which help is asked. The fact that most clients present a constellation of problems has several implications. In the premarital group, where frequently there is no problem in the usual sense of difficulty, it partly reflects the fact that the young people who have an opportunity to talk things over freely with a counselor raise various areas of discussion. Sometimes they bring up matters about which they have wondered even prior to their present relationship, such as feelings of guilt, shame, and anxiety about early sexual experiences, their attitudes toward their parents, and how these attitudes will influence their marriage. They often raise questions about present and future sexual behavior, what to expect in marriage, vocational adjustments, should the wife work, and the like.

These questions in turn are only part of the picture, since any couple, no matter how mature or well informed, has many areas of adjustment to face in planning marriage, including all the facets of getting along with each other, sexual adjustment, child spacing, budgeting and household management, as well as the practical consideration of wedding plans, specific information on marriage laws, housing, employment, and finances. Some young people are also concerned about clearing up health or other difficulties before the marriage. Any or all of these problems may be explored by premarital clients.

It is of interest in connection with premarital counseling to know something of how these marriages turn out. In a follow-up study made four months to one year after the marriage of all premaritals seen between certain dates, 89 per cent appeared to have, at that comparatively early period, satisfactory marriages. Although this series represents a small group of predominately healthy individuals, the figures are suggestive in terms of the relatively small expenditure of interviewing time necessary in certain types of premarital counseling as compared to postmarital.

When clients or patients who are having difficulty in their relationship with each other come later in marriage, they are likely to have not only a good many problems but also problems in several areas. These include sexual adjustment, situational problems, and concern about their mental health. Only a small percentage worry about their mental health; but out of 222 married clients, 72 per cent gave evidence of having significant concern about sexual problems. About 14 per cent who did report sex problems had no marital disagreements, their sex problems being related mainly to lack of information, poor technique and situational factors, or inhibiting attitudes. The more friction and hostilities present in a marriage relationship, the more likely it is that many areas in the couple's life together will be affected, including their sexual adjustment, ability to communicate in any area, enjoyment of mutual activities, disciplining of the children, relations with parents and in-laws, handling of finances, reactions to job and housework, and feelings of adequacy and personal adjustment. When the problem which is focused on sexual adjustment is found actually to be sexual adjustment rather than tension between the partners and is relieved at an early stage, it is not as likely to spread into other areas. Continued lack of sexual satisfaction, however, often leads to physical tension and irritability which may create problems in relationship or accentuate minor problems that otherwise might not be troubling. Lack of orgasm on the wife's part, especially if it appears to be linked to the husband's lack of interest in assisting his wife, may result in considerable resentment on her part, which in turn often affects other areas of the marriage.

From the counseling standpoint it is significant that marital problems usually affect more than one area in the couple's life together and are interlocking, because it often means that improvement can be made in several areas. From the point of view of mental health, all this highlights the need for medical and community resources to be available to families for the discussion of simple problems as they arise, before the problems spread into other areas of the marriage. Besides resources, there needs to be public acceptance of the fact that minor problems occur in every family and that there is advantage rather than blame in seeking outside help. Even when a problem seems relatively simple or unimportant, if it continues after the persons involved have tried to solve it themselves, help should be sought as a means of avoiding more serious complications.

For the sake of convenience, we have divided these problems into the general fields of *premarital* and *postmarital* adjustments. The premarital includes the influences of the family and the religious and moral attitudes of the community on the growing individual. Marital adjustments include sexual behavior, as well as the interaction of the family influences each partner has brought into the marriage and the problems of separation and divorce. These categories cover a multitude of practical problems, from the anxious mother who wants advice on how to tell Junior the facts of life to the man of sixty who is concerned about his loss of sexual potency.

In my experience, talking about these problems is difficult for everyone but especially difficult for a man. It is peculiarly distasteful to him to have to work on his interpersonal relationships; he is anxious and unaware and repressed when he is confronted by interpersonal problems. For a woman, I think, the task is not usually so difficult. It is important for people to have an opportunity to talk about things that they ordinarily do not talk about, because couples will go literally for years holding resentments, dissatisfactions, and troubles within themselves that they will not talk over—perhaps least of all with their partners. Then when they do start talking, it all comes out in a burst of anger and irritation which is very difficult to handle.

It is naïve to believe that one person helps another merely by saying "Now, now, this isn't so serious" or "Lots of people have trouble like yours." Ways of effective counseling that bring about catharsis, reeducation, confidence, and change are illuminated in the many actual cases cited by the various contributors to this volume. The theory and practice of effective counseling are elaborately explored in Part IV.

We have learned from the practice of experienced counselors that lasting help for people with problems in sex and marriage enables the individual to form new perspectives in his personality and on his problems, to view his own decisions and choices, to have confidence in his own abilities, and to begin to use himself in new and more constructive ways. In other words, lasting help makes it possible for the individual to help himself to solve his own problems.

In the long run this broader concept of self-knowledge in marriage and sex must replace biological as well as judgmental moralistic narrowness. The magnitude of marital unhappiness in this country as seen from indices of psychosocial friction—increasing divorce, juvenile delinquency, alcoholism, and psychosomatic and psychoneurotic conditions—makes this replacement imperative. How great a burden is thus placed on society can be seen from the staggering fact that mental illness in this country cost five billion dollars in 1956.

This book—and the course in which the material it contains had its original framework—is only a step, a small effort to familiarize those most immediately concerned with new ways of approaching these important problems. A great amount of applied psychology, sociology, and research in handling emotional and social problems lies before us. As we feel our way ahead toward understanding the emotional relationships in marriage and sex, we might bear in mind this advice to a young man from Samuel Johnson: "Sir, I would advise no man to marry who is not likely to propagate understanding."

Chapter 2

The Special Task of Premarital Counseling

EMILY HARTSHORNE MUDD, Ph.D.

MARRIAGE counseling is one of the new approaches mentioned in the preceding chapter toward the development of greater competence and satisfaction in interpersonal relations. Marriage counseling services throughout this country are geared essentially to work with the ordinary run of everyday persons. They are not legal, medical, or psychiatric clinics, nor do they give legal, medical, or psychiatric service. At the Marriage Council of Philadelphia, when people need legal advice they are referred to a Legal Aid Society or private lawyer; when they need medical examination they are referred to a hospital clinic or private physician. Of the people who have come to us over the years, 8 to 15 per cent only have been referred for psychiatric treatment. This figure follows pretty closely the one in ten figure that is quoted so often by people in the mental-health field: that is, one out of every ten persons in the United States at some time has some deep-seated difficulty that needs psychiatric attention and hospital treatment.

Marriage counseling in most cities offers service to men and women before and after marriage on a sliding-fee basis. In Philadelphia it is a nonprofit service, available to anyone in the community regardless of race, creed, or national origin. It is staffed by professionally trained social caseworkers, physicians, and clinical psychologists. About a third to a fourth of the clients come before marriage and about two-thirds after.

Since this section of the book deals with the making and breaking of marriage, it seems appropriate to discuss how people move into a marriage—the feelings and aspirations that are natural at such a time, the anxieties and disappointments, and some of the ways in which one person can help another. Before marriage, couples or individuals come for marriage counseling for reasons that fall into three general classifications. First, there are those clients who desire what is called "general preparation" for marriage. This classification consists of the young person who simply wants to talk over his feelings and attitudes about his marriage and have the opportunity to personalize the information he has obtained elsewhere, but who, as he sees it, does not have a *problem.*

Second, there is the young individual or couple who have a specific or focused problem such as "My parents disapprove" or "The girl I am in love with describes having some kind of seizures when she was a child which sound like epilepsy. What does this mean in terms of marriage?" There may be any number of specifics, but the person is focused on his particular situation, knows what he wants, uses the service for that, and moves on.

The third group, which used to be the smallest, has increased appreciably in the last decade. It consists of people who may come in after the wedding presents have been received and the announcements printed and say to the counselor: "We are to be married next week, the presents are in, my fiancé is sitting outside, my parents know that I have come here, but nobody knows what I'm going to tell you, which is that I simply cannot go through with the wedding." The counselor may have just a few hours to grapple with the problem. He must evaluate whether the person is really going to go to pieces—is she in such a state of anxiety and difficulty that the counselor should fly into action, talk to the parents, and play for time by urging postponement of the wedding—or does she merely need reassuring that everyone has natural anxiety and is a little or a great deal afraid of entering into something that cannot be experienced until it is entered into? Should the counselor add that once this step into the unknown is taken, the fear and anxiety usually dissipate?

Any such decision requires mature, subtle, and quick judgment on the part of the counselor. It must take into account the personality strength or frailty of the client, the degree of stress that may produce his saturation level, and the amount of give or flexibility that may be mustered in the family situation. In such instances the counselor, as he explores the situation, usually uncovers a multitude of difficulties. It becomes obvious that he is dealing with an individual (or two individuals) who has real personality immaturities—conflicts and emotional disturbances that will necessitate considerable work over a period of time to modify. Or if the symptoms do not seem readily reversible, he must be prepared to interpret to the client help of a more intensive nature and prepare him for referral to psychotherapy. In this third category the counselor is dealing with the realities of the calendar. He has to judge what can be done in a relatively short time and what his responsibility is in stirring up anxiety and worries that he may sense but of which the client himself may not be cognizant. He must decide, in the case of the wedding, whether it would be preferable to coast along with plans for the wedding and try to make the client feel sufficiently comfortable to come back for counseling after marriage, at which time she may recognize the problem areas and be ready to work on them.

Analysis of our agency intake indicates that the first group of clients—those who wish to use marriage counseling for education or reeducation and the allaying of natural anxiety—is decreasing and that the complicated, involved situations are becoming more frequent. We do not know the reason for this trend; but we believe that in all probability the number of marriage courses that are now being given in schools and colleges all over the country may be filling the needs of the majority of predominantly healthy young people as they move into marriage. In addition, the great amount of easily available educational literature in this field—books, pamphlets, and magazines—also serves to answer many questions and doubts and so may eliminate further need to personalize feelings by coming into such a service as a Marriage Council.

Of course, in a premarital educational service it is hoped that couples will come well ahead of definitive dates, when there is not too much pressure, and when they can explore their situation and how they feel about it in several interviews. (This is an example of the use of counseling made in the first case presented in this chapter.) One of the positive dynamics in premarital counseling is that usually the people are young, under twenty-five or thirty years. There is an opportunity to work with them before too many reaction patterns are set up in the individual personality and when they are presumably more flexible, or less rigid, and hopefully more openminded to new and different perspectives in terms of relationships.

The following two summarized case histories will illustrate situations in the categories mentioned. They will be discussed from the point of view of what can realistically be expected in premarital counseling: some of the things counselors can do, some of the things counselors cannot do, and some of the inevitable limitations of the procedure.

The first case is that of a client who came for counseling with a specific problem and later reapplied when he wanted to discuss general premarital problems. The second case is a problem situation with a rather unhappy outcome in terms of what counseling was able to do.

Mr. X was an unmarried young Protestant man of about twenty-five years who came for counseling with a specific, focused problem. He had a high-school degree and was working as an apprentice engineer. He had read about the Marriage Council and so referred himself. An unsophisticated young man with an apparently pleasant personality, it was evident that it had taken considerable courage for him to come and discuss his problem. His counselor happened to be a woman. (Both men and women counselors are available, and if anyone wishes a counselor of a particular sex, it is so arranged, if possible.) Mr. X said almost immediately that he was anticipating marriage and was concerned whether masturbation since adolescence would affect his ability to make a satisfactory sexual adjustment. Incidentally, it is not unusual for men in the premarital group to feel considerable anxiety on this subject. Mr. X was very embarrassed at first and flushed and wriggled in his chair. But as the counselor explained that there was nothing unique in this type of behavior and that the Kinsey material has made it clear that masturbation is a fairly common practice among both sexes, he gradually relaxed and talked with more comfort.

Mr. X then described his childhood home in a farming district, where he had quite naturally witnessed animal sexual behavior. This was his only means of sex instruction, having received none from his parents. Somewhere he had heard that masturbation might make him impotent and unable to satisfy his wife. Now that he was interested in a specific girl, many questions were raised in his mind about himself. He felt he should understand his condition before he asked the girl to marry him.

The counselor spent considerable time discussing the naturalness and usualness of this means of release of sexual tension before marriage, and stated that there was certainly no need to worry about his sexual adjustment in marriage just because of this. Masturbation now and then for an unmarried person was not only not abnormal but the expression of a normal biological urge. Some reading on this subject was suggested in one of the sex manuals which Mr. X was able to take home with him from the office lending library.

Mr. X then talked eagerly of the possibility of his forthcoming marriage and of his present living situation. Several months earlier he had become acquainted with a girl whom he felt sure he loved and wanted to marry. He had worked steadily since school at a good job and was looking forward to early promotion. Aside from the anxiety about his sexual habits, Mr. X felt that there was no presenting problem. Both he and his girl had similar ideals and standards, enjoyed the same forms of recreation, had many mutual friends, and were of the same religious group. The families of both young people were not very different and approved of the match.

Mr. X explained that if he became engaged he would like to bring his fiancée for a general premarital discussion. The counselor raised the question of a premarital physical examination with a physician which is routinely suggested. The meaning of such an examination for him and for his girl was explored.

Since Mr. X still seemed anxious at the end of the hour, the counselor suggested that he talk with an understanding physician to see if any other points of view came up. He was referred to a male physician experienced in premarital work who would also be equipped to see his fiancée if she decided on a premarital examination. The physician reported later that Mr. X was in good condition physically and mentally and had been helped greatly by his interview at Marriage Council. He had asked further questions about anatomy and physiology and retained some worry about "confessing" his masturbation to his fiancée. The physician noted: "She'll probably never ask and he shouldn't unload to her."

Nothing more was heard from this young man for about five months, when he phoned the counselor. He told of being officially engaged and of wanting a general premarital interview for himself and his fiancée. He mentioned he had been much helped by his previous interview and later by Dr. C. However, he asked the counselor please to refrain from mentioning his worry about masturbation, inasmuch as he had not discussed it with his fiancée and it was his impression that both the counselor and the doctor thought this unnecessary. The counselor assured him of confidentiality. Mr. X and Miss Y were seen first by the counselor for a short time. The fiancée seemed to be a bright, intelligent, attractive girl with a definite mind of her own. They talked about arrangements for the wedding, the attitudes of their parents, and about living in a furnished apartment and not with their parents.

Following this the counselor asked Miss Y if she would care to talk with her alone as Mr. X had formerly. It is routine at Marriage

Council in working with a premarital couple to give each partner the opportunity of seeing the counselor individually and then in a short joint interview. The philosophy behind this procedure is that these two individuals are going into a marriage that involves *two persons,* and the very fact of talking together to the counselor contains a healthy dynamic.

However, in this instance, Miss Y announced she saw no reason to talk to the counselor alone, saying that her fiancé had bought several books on marriage which they had been reading and discussing together freely, and she felt that anything she or the counselor or her fiancé had to say could be said in a joint interview. As Mr. X did not disagree with his fiancée's point of view the interview was continued jointly.

Miss Y had no specific problems but wanted information and free discussion of the question of child spacing. When the counselor described the statistical success of various methods of child spacing, she was able to express considerable hesitation about a physical examination before marriage—even with a woman physician. She just didn't want to go to anybody, man or woman. So it was finally worked out that her husband-to-be would use prophylactics and that she would go a month or so after marriage for a medical examination. She stated one of her reasons for not wanting a premarital examination was that her mother was opposed to her having the hymen broken before marriage. After further discussion, the couple agreed to disagree in this matter, although he was disappointed. Both expressed appreciation of being able to talk these things over and volunteered to cooperate in any follow-up after marriage. The counselor had explained that routinely Marriage Council liked to be in touch with couples that they saw before marriage after their marriage to obtain information on their adjustment.

A month after the marriage, a medical report from the physician who had talked to Mr. X before marriage found Mrs. X normal—estimated her expected sexual adjustment as good and advised her in a method of child spacing suitable for her. Again, approximately six months after marriage, the usual time for Marriage Council follow-up, they filled out the marriage-adjustment schedules [1] and came for an interview. They indicated satisfaction

[1] Background, engagement, and marriage-adjustment schedules can be ordered from Marriage Council on the request of professional persons.

with their occupations and way of living in their own quarters. Each stated they got along well with their parents and in-laws, although there was some difficulty between Mrs. X and her father-in-law and a little with Mr. X and his mother. They shared responsibility for daily household tasks, buying of supplies, and budgeting and both liked household activities. They participated together in a varied assortment of responsibilities and pleasurable activities, confiding in each other about most things. Both indicated satisfaction with their sexual adjustment, and in talking with them this appeared to be rounded and very complete. They worked out disagreements by give and take, and both rated their marriage as very happy.

Another basic rule in Marriage Council is that the counselor, in discussing child spacing and in referring the client to a local Planned Parenthood Clinic or private physician, must know and carefully consider the religious background of the client and the moral and emotional conflicts that may be engendered by such a discussion. This is particularly true when the contemplated behavior is in conflict with the dictates of the client's religious group. When the client is a member of the Catholic Church, for instance, all counselors are instructed to suggest that she discuss the matter with her priest and with a Catholic physician. In an interreligious or in an interracial marriage, the counselor has to consider the cultural patterns and pressures and their effect upon the emotional adjustment of the client. We feel that there is no place in the counseling situation for a counselor to say to a client: "You *should use* contraceptives in order to make a good adjustment." However, where there are medical implications the counselor *should* advise that the health situation be discussed with a physician.

The case we have just described pinpoints certain aspects of Marriage Council's philosophy: The counselor should be able to deal with feelings about sexual relationships as a natural part of premarital work and should not undertake such interviews until he is comfortable in discussing such material. We also assume a familiarity with the pamphlets and reading matter that through experience have been found useful as a supplement to counseling in such matters. From experience we have learned that counselors should not recommend that a client read material that they are not thoroughly familiar with themselves or unwilling to discuss objectively if the client comes back with anxiety aroused by the reading or with practical questions. Many times we find that the written word relieves anxiety. People see that others have the same questions that they do and can even say the same words. Often this material repeats what the counselor has discussed and so reinforces the new ideas. In this context it is clear that sometimes counseling includes what might be thought of as educational material, in particular where persons lack information or want to explore the information they have in terms of their own personal feelings and needs.

The second case situation is in no sense a Pollyanna story. Of the clients who come for marriage counseling, there are invariably a certain number whom counseling is unable to assist and a few who even retrogress in spite of efforts to help. Actually, the detailed evaluation of the results of counseling at Marriage Council of Philadelphia, under grants from the Public Health Service, indicate that 5 per cent of cases showed retrogression, 25 to 30 per cent showed no movement, and 60 to 65 per cent or about two-thirds showed varying degrees of improvement.[2] Put another way, some situations improve and other situations do not seem to change, but the clients' attitudes modify and they feel better and so handle their problems better. Occasionally neither the situation improves nor does the client feel better. Sometimes the client does not return or let the agency know what happens or even moves away so that he cannot be found for follow-up contact.

Mr. A, twenty-six, and Miss C, twenty-five, had completed graduate professional training and were beginning professional jobs when they first came for premarital interviews. Miss C had

[2] See footnote, p. xxiv.

heard about marriage counseling during a marriage course at her coeducational college and referred herself when she was planning marriage. By arranging appointments, she felt "she was doing everything she should to help prepare herself adequately for marriage." Mr. A, who was rather skeptical about the procedure, postponed his interview until just before the wedding. Miss C moved immediately into a discussion of sexual adjustment, considering herself well informed from reading and looking forward to this aspect of marriage. She emphasized the importance to her of having a job and of her father's feeling of wanting her to be an adequate professional person. She stated that she and her fiancé agreed on the *"absolute necessity* of postponing any children until her husband was making an adequate income and until she was well established in her career."

Miss C did not want to talk about the attitudes of the parents toward the marriage, or the matter of any personality difference between her and her fiancé. She stated she anticipated no problems and had come to discuss sexual adjustment and to get details about child spacing and a referral for premarital examination. She was referred to a physician experienced in premarital examinations who reported that she was in good health and had been instructed in a method of contraception that for her he estimated was 95 per cent success. He added she was cooperative and intelligent during examination.

A few days before the wedding Mr. A came for his appointment. He raised many more questions than his fiancée and seemed less sure of himself in relation to marriage and its responsibilities. He felt uncertain that he could keep up with the demands of his work and at the same time satisfy his future wife's needs. He felt his fiancée's family were all very close, better off financially, and socially superior to his family. He resented this and did not feel sure of his in-laws' acceptance of him. However, he believed that inasmuch as he and Miss C would be financially independent, due to her job, and as they planned to live in a different community, her parents could be dismissed from the picture. Further exploration of Mr. A's doubts and ambivalent feelings was suggested by the counselor. He admitted that this would have been a good idea, but actually there was no time as the wedding was scheduled for three days hence.

In such a situation there is little that the counselor can do beyond establishing an ongoing relationship which, hopefully, can be renewed after the wedding. If the counselor should press additional questions in response to the client's anxiety, it could result in his being unable to continue with the wedding plans or the subsequent marriage relationship and thus precipitate a real crisis. We felt the prognosis was poor and that in all probability there would be difficulty in the relationship.

The routine follow-up, instigated about four months after the marriage, indicated things had gone fairly well for the first few months and that a mutually satisfying sexual adjustment had been begun, although with some difficulty. Then about two months later Mrs. A wrote that she was unexpectedly pregnant and terribly upset. She had done everything recommended by "the marriage experts," and her reward was bitter disillusionment. She showed intense anger toward "the experts" and toward her husband and the marriage. She was determined to continue her job and would give the baby to her mother to take care of. The counselor felt even less optimistic and again suggested to Mr. and Mrs. A the importance of a series of interviews to work through some of their very strong feelings. But neither the young husband nor the wife saw any point in such a plan, "because intelligent people could and should work out their own problems."

No word came from this couple for five years, and then to the counselor's surprise, Mrs. A called for an appointment requesting priority on the waiting list on the basis of having been a premarital client. She depicted a badly deteriorated marriage relationship, very poor sexual adjustment since the birth of the baby, and a continuing fear of another unplanned pregnancy. She had been fooled once by "the experts" and had no trust in anyone, including her husband for whom she had also lost respect. She indicated disagreements over her living in a separate apartment, continuing her job, and letting her mother raise the child. She admitted a need for help and planned a series of counseling interviews.

The next week Mr. A also applied for counseling, showing evidence of being badly threatened, insecure, and very unhappy at his wife's continuing rejection of him sexually and in other spheres. As his anxiety increased he felt impotent at times, which worried him terribly. Even trying an affair with someone other than his wife did not restore his self-confidence. This sense of failure and generalized anxiety were being reflected in his professional work and other activities. He resented deeply his wife's turning to her family and their protection of her and the child, which he felt relieved her of responsibility of coming to grips with marriage and the care of her own baby. During the weekly individual counseling for the wife and husband, each seeing the same counselor, there was some improvement in the relationship. Each began to recognize that both partners had to put something into the marriage as well as into their jobs, that they had to give as well as get through this relationship, and that there were responsibilities that could be enjoyed through sharing. However, the pattern of pain and bitterness had been so intense that they had little desire left to make a go of their present relationship. Feelings of comfort and love were so far lost that the prognosis for success seemed continuingly poor. As this realization became a reality to both, their anxiety increased, their feelings of self-esteem and of adequacy lessened, and they became even more threatened. The idea of moving into a divorce was basically traumatic to each; it was not in their concept of family or professional life.

At this stage in counseling it seemed obvious that Mr. and Mrs. A were deeply disturbed and that each was questioning his total personality organization. Therefore psychiatric referral was suggested by the counselor. After careful consideration each moved into psychiatric treatment, and the report about two years later indicated that they had divorced. It is hoped that following this they would begin their life again with increased insight into their own needs and increased potentiality for constructive use of their abilities. Recognizably, psychiatry cannot guarantee such results.

Marriage Council's first contact with the couple occurred at a premarital interview, at which time the counselor was aware of basic potential problems of rigidity, control, insecurity, and anxiety. However, because of the attitude of the two persons involved and the nearness of the wedding date, it seemed impossible to accomplish anything beyond their specific requests. In this particular situation, the presenting cause of the beginning deterioration in the marriage seemed to be the stresses and frustrations of the unexpected pregnancy. Whether if this had not happened something else essentially disturbing would have come up is of course not known. But where there is a basically sound relationship between partners, an unplanned pregnancy is usually assimilated into the total situation and the adjustment becomes even firmer. In this case, however, Mrs. A was unable to assimilate the frustration and disappointment involved. Instead of using counseling when the acute problem began, which might have held real potential for assistance, she projected her difficulties and bitterness onto her husband and gradually through the ensuing five years almost emasculated him. The final results of this destructive interaction drove her, and through her the husband, to seek counseling and later, with less pressure and more understanding of the depth of their need, to apply for psychotherapy. This case illustrates what is not always realized, that you *cannot force* people to use counseling help at the time when the problem is obvious only to the counselor anymore than you can force them to use medical help. Counseling cannot accomplish miracles, nor indeed can it accomplish anything unless the persons, themselves, have the will to work on their problems.

To summarize our procedures and philosophy in premarital counseling: we consider this phase of our work potentially more difficult, subtle, and obviously open to hazards in terms of goals and results than any other type of work that comes to a marriage counseling service. This is in contrast to what professional people in our postgraduate in-service training program usually think. "Give us a nice, easy premarital to start with," they say. And in this "nice, easy premarital," all the counselor usually knows about the couple when they telephone for an appointment is that they are going to be married in a week or a month and that they want a premarital interview. In such an appointment a counselor may face something like the complicated case just described or he may run into a more simple situation. In recent years records at Marriage Council indicate he is much more likely to be confronted with the hazardous situation.

Elsewhere [3] I have made some comments on this subject which I would like now to repeat:

"Premarital counseling can be thought of in relation to the whole process of physical and emotional growing up, a time primarily of transition from life within the parents' family to life in a new family. As such, many of the patterns of childhood and adolescent relationship behavior with the father and mother are reenacted in terms of the new relationship with the partner. Such processes reflecting earlier emotional conflicts call for time and thoughtful, dignified consideration. And yet often in premarital work the counselor must deal with reality time limits already inherent in the situation, limits which are out of the control of the individual client or counselor but which result from the general ritual in our culture leading to marriage. This usually involves, in sequence, announcement to the community of the intention to marry, the giving of a ring, and finally the setting of a date for the ceremony. The period when a premarital client comes to a counseling office is often therefore one of considerable stress. Sometimes it occurs a few days before an engagement announcement, or a week before a wedding. Counseling plans must often be laid and effected within these situational limits. Ideally, they should be laid several months in advance of the wedding.

"In the United States in 1956 little more than three hundred professionally staffed urban services officially offer marriage counseling as the whole or part of their listed service. With an over-all figure of some 36,635,000 married couples reported in the 1951 census and 381,000 divorces in the same year, or a rate of 10.4 divorces per 1,000 married couples, it appears obvious that considerable suffering and instability are currently reflected

[3] Emily H. Mudd, "Premarital Counseling," Chapter 6 in *The Medical Practitioner's Contributions toward Healthy Emotional Development* (The Physician as a Counselor), J. B. Lippincott Company, Philadelphia, 1957 (in press). Ed. by Samuel Liebman, M.D.

in family living in our culture. Recent reports suggest, perhaps optimistically, that much of this could be alleviated or eliminated by education, reeducation, interest, caring, sharing and common-sense perspective.

"In addition to the physical examinations required by law, talking things over with another human being is admittedly relieving to the puzzled and anxious person. However, whether constructive re-orientation of lasting value results from this relationship depends on two basic factors. First and of primary importance, the attitude, ability and will to do of the person who desires to learn and has a difficulty, and secondly the skill of the person who serves officially as a counselor. Here, the counselor's ability to furnish the information necessary in a relaxed and comfortable manner and to function as a sounding board that reflects to the troubled person with warmth and friendliness his own actions and feelings, is of paramount importance. This process helps such a person to mobilize his potentialities for change, aids him to obtain perspective and opens new vistas for future goals.

"A few physicians and counselors from other professions have such natural gifts, and to them flock friends and acquaintances who find and carry away from this contact consolation, strength, and encouragement. Certain doctors and other would-be counselors seek to impose on the person seeking help their own value judgments, their own unachieved goals or unrecognized biases, bitterness and frustrations. Such procedure rather than enabling the troubled person to more comfortable functioning may only confuse, burden and further handicap him.

"Persons troubled by lack of information and disturbed feelings or problem situations in the interpersonal relations of courtship, engagement and marriage, failing a naturally helpful friend or family member, will most easily have contact before marriage with a teacher, a minister or a physician. Because of the legal requirements for marriage, every young person in the large majority of our states must have a medical certificate involving contact with a physician. Therefore, the doctor has the greatest opportunity at present in our culture for first-hand exploration and guidance. The minister has a similar unparalleled opportunity with those many young persons who seek a church wedding. And in an increasing number of communities carefully trained marriage counselors are available to anyone who wishes to use them, in services which can helpfully supplement those of the doctor and the minister. Premarital counseling need not in many instances be overly time consuming. Counseling before marriage can deal at an incipient level with potential problems and thus lay foundations for the promotion of competence and comfort in the relationship between man and wife and for the avoidance of later acute conflict which so often is the precursor of physical, emotional and spiritual illness."

Chapter 3

Normal and Abnormal in Psychosexual Development

LEON J. SAUL, M.D.

IN THE light of our present knowledge, individual personality characteristics with their potential for growth and modification appear to be of primary importance in interpersonal relationships. Thus an understanding of personality development is basic to an understanding of the interaction between men and women in courtship, engagement, and marriage, between parent and child, and in other close contacts of daily living. This chapter spells out the perspectives for the normal and abormal in psychosexual development.

There are three main facts about the development of the total personality to bear in mind. The first is the progressive development of a fertilized egg cell to responsible, productive independence. The cell begins as completely parasitic upon the maternal organism, and becomes a being no longer dependent but mobile in its own right and able to do things—to get food for itself, to get shelter for itself, and even to take care of other creatures. During its early stage of life the infant is passive. It needs to have things done for it. It is also receptive—it must be fed, washed and clothed. Because it could not survive if it were not for the mother—and giving some credit after birth to the

30

father—the infant is dependent. The pattern in infancy one could call roughly: passive, receptive, dependent.

On the other hand consider the position of adults as husbands and wives. As parents we are supposed to be responsible, independent, and productive. Now there is a great difference between the growth of the organism from the state of passivity, receptivity, dependence to responsibility, independence, productivity. This is one of the striking facts about biological growth, personality, and sexual development.

Being independent does not mean that the person is a hermit and goes off and lives on the top of a mountain somewhere without relationships to other people. It means he is no longer dependent in the sense that the child is dependent upon the parents. There is a great difference between the interdependence of social and family life and the dependence of the child.

The second fact that strikes one as being central and significant about the emotional life is this: Along with the drive of the organism to become big and strong and independent, to reproduce and take care of the young also, there is, strangely enough, a counterforce, a tendency for the organism to return to an earlier state. I do not know whether this is a basically biological tendency, but certainly it is seen in human beings psychologically.

To give a simple example, let us take a man who had a very difficult childhood. His story is not quite rags to riches but rags to middle class. He worked himself up with very little in the way of affection or emotional or financial support. He gets married, has four children, and does pretty well in business. He has a business partner who gives him rather more emotional support than he realizes. He is able to share his problems with the partner, discuss his worries, weep on his shoulder a bit. One day the partner leaves. When this happens the man suddenly becomes unable to work. He gives up; he cannot concentrate; he does not want to do anything but sit around the house. He sees his family being threatened with disruption and poverty by his behavior and becomes very anxious because of this, but there is not much he can do about it. Finally, he turns to psychiatric help. This man returned in part—because these regressions are usually partial—to the status of not being responsible and independent, to being threatened with having to be supported and taken care of as he was in childhood. So the second striking fact about the emotional and sexual development is the counterforce or *regressive tendency*.

The third important point to note is the extreme *conditionability* of human beings. In the course of clinical practice, I never cease wondering at the enormous conditionability of the human cortex, the extent to which the later adult tree of the human being has been bent as a twig in childhood by emotional forces. A person has very accepting, loving, devoted parents who are always delighted to see him, and his attitude toward life and other groups may be: "You lucky people, here I am." Another person perhaps lost his parents as a child and was given to relatives. They do not want him and pass him on to other relatives. Thus he grows up without a sense of security or acceptance. He goes around fastening himself onto everyone to be sure that he is accepted and that he gets some love. And underneath it all he has a resentful, hollow•feeling that in reality he is never going to be loved; he is going to be deserted—in other words, that he will wind up in the situation in which he lived in childhood.

Now armed with these three important points about emotional development—the progressive drives to maturity, the regressive tendency, and the conditionability—what can we say about the development of the personality? This, I think, depends mostly upon what one calls "personality." Freud's formulation of the personality is simple and provides a useful tool. It works in actual psychiatric practice with patients and helps us to understand people. This concept of personality is tripartite and is derived by grouping the many emotional forces and mental functions in a simple, usable way consistent with known facts and theories.

First are the biological animal drives (progressive and regressive). To emphasize the biochemical impersonal nature of these forces, Freud called the reservoir of these in the organism the *id*. Eventually the regressive tendency to return to a previous state prevails in the form of death. Nobody can escape his own life cycle: the development, the span of maturity, and the decline.

The second motivation in personality is called the *superego*, which includes the conscience. The superego comprises the effects of childhood conditioning, the way the individual has lived in childhood—whether he has been loved or unloved, feels dominated or feels rebellious against domination. The results of these conditioning experiences, operating as the superego, shape and color each person's view of the world. The superego is an internal mechanism that largely determines our accustomed, automatic ways of meeting the outside world.

The third group of mental functions is called the *ego*, which includes our consciousness and all the functions related to it. These functions are of three main kinds: perceptive, integrative, and executive. There are perhaps more, but I think this is the most logical grouping. We perceive the outside world, our inner needs, and the activity of our conscience. We try to integrate these perceptions, and we then have definite functions of the ego such as judgment, will, and control to guide our behavior. We perceive what it is we want, gauge the situation in the world, and sense the effects of conscience and training; we integrate these together and so direct our actions.

Now if things go relatively well, if we can satisfy our id needs in the outer world in harmony with the effects of our training and conscience, we feel good. We try to enjoy life and our relations with others; we love and are loved. All these good feelings —all the unifying tendencies to love and be loved, to give and receive, all that is in any sense libidinal—can be subsumed under the term Eros. If things *do not* go well, we get angry, and even if they do go well, we eventually die. Anger, hate, aggression, debility, fear—this destructive direction is covered by the term Thanatos, the Greek word for death.

Of course, originally everything is id, as in the primitive fetal animal organism. The differentiated parts of the id we call the ego and the superego. If the conditioning influences help human development, we naturally get a proper, mature human being— something that is not commonly encountered. Usually things go wrong in the conditioning and there is some form of trouble, so that the development is warped or interrupted, fixated, as it is called.

In the case of the man mentioned earlier, he grows up, supports his family, works well, meets responsibility, but when he meets with an emotional bump, things go wrong and he begins to go to pieces and has what is generally termed a nervous breakdown. If the conditioning does not work right we find people who in adult life still have the characteristics of children, or else they seem to grow and develop and function well, but under some sort of stress they break down and return—"regress"—to the childhood pattern. An example of fixation is found in Dr. Strecker's writing on Momism which describes the boy who has not adequately emancipated himself from the dependent attachment to his mother.

With this description of the personality and the forces at play within it, we now have a perspective in which to examine the sexual development.

If we group together under the term Eros all that is libidinal, all the good feelings, the dependent needs, the wishes for love, and the giving of love, including that within families and between friends and others, we come out with a very broad view. This is the position that Freud developed at the end of his life. I think it is a useful idea, although many people do not. According to this point of view, there is a life force that tends to bring together inert matter into the form of living cells. The same force can bring together many individual cells into multicellular organisms like ourselves. These organisms, in turn, can get together sexually to reproduce a family. They can also get together into social organizations, and in this view society may also be motivated by similar cohesive libidinal forces. People like to get together and be together—animals do, too.

If this is true, then sex must be understood in terms of a much broader concept than the one often used. It turns out to be a more involved and complex thing than genital sensations to which the older view restricted it. Certainly sex is part of the mating instinct. But the mating instinct is more than sex alone. Often families are held together when there is no sexual activity between the parents, or when sex takes peculiar forms. Certainly the tendency to mate involves more than local chemical activity.

Mating also involves love, which is connected with sex. Love is a force that keeps the family together presumably for the purpose—and here I do not hesitate to be somewhat teleological —of rearing the young, a biological function. So there is love between parents in those forms that have the parental family and there is love certainly from the mother to the offspring in some degree. Otherwise, I suppose, the offspring would not survive. Sex is a part of mating, but mating has to do with love or is part of love. But love is not confined to the family alone. We love our friends; we love our country. Love becomes also a broader thing than something that is merely part of sex or merely part of mating.

This means, then, that we should distinguish between (1) sex, (2) love, and (3) mating and marriage. A person can have a great deal of sexual activity. He can have it with prostitutes or in some other form in which there is little in the way of love and little or nothing that can be called mating. You can also have a great lover, a Casanova, who never mates in the sense of getting married. On the other hand if one were fortunate, it would be possible to get a combination of the sexual and great romantic love with somebody who was also a good wife and mother or husband and father. I think that many young people and many who come to the physician or counselor for guidance have these three elements confused in their minds. These forces are related, but sex, love, and the capacity for marital relationship, although overlapping, are three separate things. (This interrelationship is elaborated by Dr. Roche in the next two chapters.)

Another point about sex is that any strong feeling can be sexualized. Now I suppose this is because the sex hormones are racing around in our bloodstreams, and if we get ideas about this, that, or the other thing, there is always enough effect upon our cortical cells from these hormones to tie up these other things with sex. Actually any strong feeling can achieve sexual coloring. An example would be sadism where the main activity is a cruel or hostile one but practiced because the individual gets sexual pleasure out of it. He may thereby reach orgasm, and in the perversion, not only does he get orgasm through cruel behavior but may be unable to achieve it in other ways. Thus an impulse that is the opposite of love, a destructive impulse, can become sexualized.

Furthermore, sex is a form of emotional expression, a pathway for many emotions. When a person gets emotionally tense, it can be due to all sorts of different things such as fear or anger; but he turns to sexual activity as a way of getting relaxation and of draining the tension. At the same time sex is often stimulated by impulses that are really foreign to it and have nothing to do with it. It is certainly a striking factor in the sense of consolation. Frustration and anger can also arouse it. A businessman I know would get into a meeting where there would be a great deal of give and take and would feel frustrated and get keyed up when things did not go the way he wanted them to. As a result, he would become uncontrollably aroused sexually and have to go out and do something about it in order to drain his feelings.

Another situation that occurs frequently is for sex to be used to act out an emotional expression. For example, here is a girl with a frankly erotic personality, yet she leads the man on and then turns him down cold and completely rejects him. Here sex is used to get somebody into a situation where he could then be rejected. Why does she do it? Because she was conditioned by, and returning to, an early pattern. She had been very much rejected by her father, whereupon she turned from him to a near relative for a little understanding and acceptance and did not get it. Thus rejected in turn by him, she began to develop a pattern of rejecting others as she herself had been rejected.

We see that sex colors much of the human scene. In reading the literature in this field, however, it is important to distinguish between sex as sensuality and sex as the psychological feeling we call love. The term is used both ways in the literature and rather interchangeably so that when an article starts to deal with the sexual life and talks about people being in love, it is difficult to know whether the author is talking about sensuality or love.

In order to understand the meaning of sensuality we will run through its history briefly. It is not known at what precise point subjective sensations begin. If the fetus has sensations I suppose they are in the skin, which has contact with the amniotic fluid, and in the muscles that kick around. Soon after the infant is born, sucking starts. He sucks his food, thumb, and anything else he can get hold of, and apparently gets pleasurable sensation from so doing. These sensations are called *oral* because they occur around the mouth. Next the infant gets teeth and starts to bite things, getting sensations from chewing. Also, the baby has to be kept clean, have his diapers changed, the process becoming more of an issue when he is a year or two old and more attention is given to cleanliness in general. In the second year, there is an emphasis on elimination and training. Later, the importance of anal sensation becomes apparently more or less secondary to genital sensation. At that point the child usually discovers his genitals and to some extent shows an interest in masturbation. These phases cannot be numbered with any sharpness according to age because there is great variation in different children and the phases can overlap and persist with each other. Here I have to introduce a psychological element. The sexual feelings can involve other persons in childhood just as well as all the other sensations arising from suckling, eating, toilet training, muscular activity, which are all supervised by and related to others. In the child, sex is still on the level of play; the properly matured adult requires a heterosexual object, with whom the earlier sensual feelings become part of the so-called foreplay.

When the genital sensations become stronger in the child, what predominates—in the boy, at any rate—is the wish for strength and masculinity. A boy, for example, is apt to have less capacity for a concern for another person than for whether he is big enough and strong enough and masculine enough. Therefore, the psychological factor at this stage is to show or ask: "Am I bigger than my brother, my sister? Am I bigger and stronger than my father?" The object relationship he grows into through this, if all goes well, is identification with men. At the same time, therefore, there arises a certain amount of masculine competition with men, in the background of which is mother or sister—women. This is probably budding male competitiveness.

This development is fundamental. If a young man gets stuck, fixated, at this point and does not develop further, he is apt to turn into a perennial adolescent. There is the story of the young man who visits a girl and puts his arms out and says: "I can do this for half an hour and Willie can only do it for fifteen minutes." Meanwhile the girl sits on the other end of the sofa. Now if he overcomes this type of behavior and detaches the interest from himself, stops worrying about whether he is being big enough and strong enough and able enough and better than Willie, if he gets to the point where he is able to be sufficiently interested in a girl to take responsibility for her—pay her bills, support her, take care of the children, and put in his day's work and then come home and put in some more work being a husband and parent—he shows object interest and sufficient strength and capacity to give, indicating that he has reached maturity and is able to marry and have a family.

Sexual maturity involves responsibility, productivity, and independence or, as it has been called technically, "object interest on the genital level." It is the capacity to be a good spouse and parent, and, of course, it involves the same capacity for constructive, friendly interest in the people with whom we work and live. We are then naturally good workers and good citizens and good mates and parents.

Chapter 4

Early Life Experience and Marriage

PHILIP Q. ROCHE, M.D.

FOUR generalizations will be developed in this chapter to serve as a model of a psychological approach to marriage problems: (1) that such conflicts in marriage have origin in early childhood; (2) that such conflicts are for the most part unconscious; (3) that conflicts have the tendency to repeat themselves in symptoms (symbols); and (4) that conflicts are modifiable in what is called therapy.

In respect to the first generalization, love life and mating can be examined, particularly as to the early determinants of behavior in the child. One of the most useful theoretical operations of modern psychiatry is based on the reassessment of symptomatic behavior in the adult in the light of antecedent adaptations of the infant and child. That is to say, the adult symptom has a natural history and is prefigured in the experience of the earlier infantile periods of psychological growth. The basis of this approach, described in detail in the preceding chapter by Dr. Saul, is that sexual as well as aggressive forces are manifest in all periods of life. This view is contradictory to the older ideas that the child is sexless and innocent and that sexual drives in particular are not active until puberty. The existence of early sexual drives rests upon observations confirmable by anyone who will take the trouble to look.

40

So far as can be determined, man's life appears to be fashioned by primary, instinctual sexuality and aggressiveness modified by learning and decision making. The instinctual endowment is modifiable during the prolonged dependency of the human child and continuously interacts with his environment, both human and material. Out of these interactions in any given culture appear an infinite variety of character and adaptive behaviors and also general characteristics. Each individual bears a similarity to his fellows, yet each is unique. The interactions between the instinctual forces and the environment of persons and things are continuous and unremitting at succeeding levels of personality development; the patterns of problem solving derived from them in time tend to become fixed in repetitive patterns.

Marital problems have antecedent determinants of causation, and as lived inwardly or acted outwardly they express in repetition an attempted mastery of early, imbedded, unbalanced psychic conflict. Such symptoms of conflict are expressions of momentary equilibrium of a kind of psychic tension with the minimum expenditure of energy. It remains for us to observe these interactions and their resolutions in the child and to trace their ultimate transformations in the marriage behavior in the adult. We may restate our premise: the behavior in the adult is a continuation of responses learned in childhood. Therefore, if we wish to speak of the meaning of disturbed marital relationships, we must shift from an exclusive focus on the adult behavior to consideration of the infantile level, and obtain a comprehensive view of the patient's total life experience of persons and things.

Out of an accumulation of observations on marriage failure, there emerge configurations of early life adaptations representing significant phases of psychic growth in the first five to seven years. We may relate these adaptations to cultural pressures exerted to modify the child's primary instincts of sexuality and aggressiveness. We may detect in adult behavior lingering elements of these earlier phases and note that when infant-child behavior continues conspicuously unmodified into adult life, we observe a symbolic behavior called "neurotic" or "perverse." The symptom of adult maladaptation in marriage can be recognized as a continuation of the infant-child maladaptation. One does not do well in the marriage relationship because one did not learn to do well in earlier relationships. Both are aspects of the love life, but with different love objects, separated in time. The fact that these situations are analogous implies that the learned behavior sets of the infant-child continue unmodified into adult life, which is an oversimplification and may be misleading. All behavior is continuously modified by time-space experience; but it is nevertheless true that the original imprint of maladaptation as expressed in latent symbol continues unchanged. The unhappiness of a marriage partner is a manifestation of unchanging symbolic behavior. The marriage partner carries out certain performances in his social reactions and love life, but he is unaware of the symbolic meaning of his behavior.[1] He does not know why he is compelled to play the role he does;

[1] Anatol Rapoport, *The Role of Symbols in Human Behavior*, Psychiatric Research Reports, no. 2, American Psychiatric Association, December, 1955.

Anatol Rapoport states: "Today, although we certainly have come to realize that no understanding of man is possible without a systematic inquiry into man's non-human environment, the subject matter of natural science, still the old feeling that symbols and language are of fundamental importance has been amply vindicated. Today we would call the 'symbolic universe' the man-made, non-material part of man's environment as much so as the web is the most important spider-made part of the spider's environment, or the metabolic products released by the bacteria in a bacterial culture are a vital part of the bacteria's environment. All these 'secreted' environments play a decisive role in the subsequent fate of each organism. Man in society 'secretes' his symbolic environment, that is, his culture, in which he must continue to live. (A fortunate coincidence in two meanings of the word 'culture' referring to a bacterial colony and to human society makes a lively metaphor possible.) This symbolic environment is instrumental in shaping man's natural environment, and is, in turn, shaped by it. Hence its crucial importance."

nor can he be changed until he is made aware of the latent meaning of his symbolic "secretions." But the analogous situations are not fully explored until we apply another psychiatric observation: the persistence of energy-bound infantile patterns operating below conscious awareness in the adult. This leads to a restatement of our premise: maladaptation in marriage is a continuation of prior maladaptation, the direct recall of which is obscured, but which is lived inwardly and acted outwardly in a highly sophisticated way as symptoms that are presented to the person from whom help is being sought.

One thinks of events not as isolated experiences of singular traumatic impact but as infant-child experiences with duration, sustained tensional qualities in the totality of intercommunication, and in a setting of significant persons. It is not enough to reconstruct early experience with the child as the prime focus; a further appreciation can be obtained only when we bring others around the child into the same focus and think of events as transactional and complementary. The remarkable feature of infant-child experience is that upon recollection so little of it is reducible to verbal communication. It remains deep in the realm of feeling and symbol. The symptomatic behavior associated with marriage failure represents the reactivation of unconscious components of early events that find devious surface expression in anxiety, nonverbal organ language of physical ill-being, and symbolic acting out. The therapist or counselor must not only decode such behavior and separate the threads of connection and meaning with early experience, but also communicate his insight in such a manner that the person seeking help can use it. People tend to seek for sexual education probably for the reason that it is withheld and tabooed in the formative years of child rearing. Because of this early circumstance, in later life sexuality carries the marks of infantile distortions; and when things go badly sexuality tends to be associated with morbidity.

This conclusion would seem to be corroborated in part by the observation that so many of the tensions of love life find ultimate expression in impotence and frigidity. Many patients are unable to convey anything of their interpersonal problems except in terms of such sexual disabilities. This physical malfunction is also a reflection of how deeply imbedded is the notion of the separation of the mind from the body, the separation of the body from the "self." The body, or part of it, is presented to the physician, but the "self" is kept out of reach. A married man was referred by a urologist who found no physical explanation for the complaint of sexual impotence. The patient had presented a part of his body to the physician, a symbolic communication in which body awareness presented as a complaint was the manifest content. But the latent content of the communication related to a larger dimension of the patient's universe. Further inquiry revealed that the patient was impotent only with his spouse and not with an illicit partner; furthermore, his impotence lay in his total life situation, extending to his social and occupational relationships as well. But the nub of his problem was that he did not know why he was impotent and could not know why until he had presented his "self" to the doctor as well as his body. The problem for the physician was how to recognize and integrate the patient's symbols.

We may now turn to what are believed to be the configurations of early events which have such power to shape and govern personality. For our purpose emphasis may be centered around the growth stresses of the first five to seven years, which span what are conventionally called the phases of psychosexual development. These phases are not entities but continuous processes, parts of which have been arbitrarily named for the sake of convenience. They are both biologically and culturally determined. The central fact, observable to everyone, is that the newborn child has a psychological and virtual physical unity with the mother and that his subsequent growth is a loosening of such primary ties from her.

In the first year the child's unity with the mother is essentially one of an oral-nutritive connection with her, associated with body contact simulating the intrauterine attachment. In psychological terms this connection means security and passive dependence. Psychobiological growth implies renunciation of this oral-passive dependency, which lingers in varying degrees in the adult and which sometimes shows itself as a character problem in wooing and marriage. Not a few women discover a baby in their husbands.

The primary oral phase of growth is supplemented by new experiences marked by an increasing area of separation from the mother and by the discipline, taboos, and ethical system of rewards and punishments imposed in toilet training. These come to the child as an initiation into a world of government, and the continuations of unresolved conflicts of this period may appear later in varying degrees of character deformation. In the extreme, the cold, rigid, compulsive, authoritarian, and sometimes sadistic view of love and marriage may find some expression here.

These oral and sphincter aspects of child experience are the substrata upon which later phases of domestication are overlaid. From the third to the seventh year the child's interests expand beyond mouth and sphincter functions to his general physical being, with the focus particularly on the genitals and their derivative pleasures and on the significance of sex difference. The child has a growing awareness of his place in the family setting, with increasing sensitivity and intensity of reaction to his parents and others in the household. With this awakening sense of individuality he lives through a critical social adaptation within the family orbit. We describe this adaptation figuratively in terms of complementary, primitive, love-hate interactions with both parents. The core of this triangu-

lar interaction is the resistance against giving up dependent possession of the mother, with variable secondary competitive struggles with others in the family.

In the normal working through of these conflicts in our culture, they are resolved through psychic repression (forgetting),
a rechanneling of sexuality and aggressiveness into social senti-
ments of parental idealization and identification, and redirection
of aggressiveness into conventional competition. The aim of the
resolution is union with a heterosexual love object. Here we are
alluding to a life experience familiar to us as the oedipus complex.

In our culture the oedipal experience is followed by a period
of relative quiescence. This is in turn succeeded by puberty, a
period of renewal and of a more sophisticated reassimilation of
the same love-hate conflicts within the family which are extended beyond the family into the school and social life. It is
during the pubertal phase of growth that we may detect tell-
tale traces of the earlier oedipal struggles; these appear in the
adolescent with the advent of secondary physical sexual development and his awakening hopes and sense of what is expected of him in his social and sexual world as a mature person. In a narrow biological sense, maturity implies the capacity
for genital union with the opposite sex. In a wide social sense
it implies the capacity for anxiety-free, nongenital love relationships. The direction taken in the resolution of the oedipal
elements will set the subsequent course in later domestication.
Often in marriage the elements are revealed in bold relief.

Many observations of love life may be viewed in the light of
the foregoing propositions. A common situation is that of early
separation of the child from the mother. Such separation can be
an actual physical separation by death, removal, or abandonment;
or, in a less obvious manner, it can be an emotional separation
reflected in disinterest and remoteness. Early separation of the
mother from the child imposes on him a threat to the passive

dependency which to him has the meaning of survival; in psychological terms, he feels the separation means he is unloved and unworthy.

Separation is met by an overdetermined response in the child, in anxiety from direct threat, and by secondary reactive hostility which has the effect of magical protest and hoped-for restitution. When things go badly, we shout louder and communicate our anger. Furthermore, these immediate responses to the loss of support do not succeed, and there is generally an associated reactive pattern of regression to an earlier stage of growth. The child becomes more babylike and demanding, wants to be fed, and may relax sphincter control. Growth gains are lost, and one must start all over again to recover them.

It is not difficult to see this pattern in ourselves when we sense the impending loss of an important person, that is, one who supports us. We feel in this situation an intensification of anxiety which is met with compensatory demands, and when these fail we withdraw. We postulate that such an early established pattern of personal survival tends to persist and activate the personality in later life, and it is not hard to detect this in many marriages. The jealous spouse overcompensates in terms of the regressive demand for support from, and exclusive possession of, one who now stands as a substitute mother image. This is descriptive of the primary reaction of running to the mother. The withdrawal is secondary; its counterpart in the adult is observed as a defense that takes the form of avoiding closeness to the loved partner and sometimes of avoiding amative relationships at all. Once hurt, one avoids being hurt again. This pattern is seldom in full awareness, and many men are able to rationalize their bachelorhood and cover the deeper reasons for their choice.

From this basic pattern other maneuvers sometimes evolve. A man may fall in love and once sure of being loved find himself compelled to desert his loved one. This is a fulfillment of the revenge motive: he is squaring an old account. Often, unless the individual attains some awareness of his inner motivations, he may go on repeating this kind of neurotic bookkeeping, like Don Juan leaving behind him a trail of broken hearts. The irony of this behavior lies in the fact that he loves in order to hate. One may observe this motif in some marriages, in which there is no clean break but a continuous loving-hating oscillation.

Another variation of this theme will come to the notice of those who deal with marital discord. A man falls in love with a woman who is sure to abandon him. She is the unconscious choice of the man who was before abandoned as a child. He may try again, and will unfailingly choose another woman sure to abandon him, at least figuratively. Here we may observe the repetitive principle of mental life and its operation and working through of traumatic experiences. Repetition is a way to mastery. Our abandoned husband will attribute his love loss either to bad luck or to the perfidy of womankind; but with some insight he may come to realize that he is attempting to achieve mastery through repetition and reenactment of the first broken romance. It may be said that when one first falls in love, it is always for the second time.

Our observations of behavior in marriage lead us to the general proposition that not only do unconscious elements lie behind the tensions of mating but that such elements must also play a part in the choice of a love partner. One's love choice is in some way a revenant of one's "first" love. When a young couple falls in love, there will be those around them ready to wonder what it was they found in each other. But find it they do. In marriage there exist second-order delineations of the determinants of love life.

Marriage is perceived as a coupling; it may also be regarded as a marriage of families who, in euphemism, are called in-laws. When we marry, we marry someone else's mother and father; the husband has two mothers and two fathers, and the wife likewise. In this situation we often note the reawakening of old infantile problems; this train of events and interactions has attained the status of a special institution, the mother-in-law. The hazards of many a marriage are thought to be the work of this woman, who is fair game in our culture and the butt of opprobrium. However, the mother-in-law problem is universal, and in many primitive societies there are erected taboo barriers in kinship that work fairly well to minimize the irrational displacements carried over from childhood to later objects within the tribe.

The stereotype of the mother-in-law as the modern counterpart of the witch exists in fact and in fantasy. The mother-in-law becomes the new object of affects displaced from the original to the substitute; this also holds true for the father-in-law. It is often noted that a young married man is still much too close to his mother or the young wife to her father. This situation is the setting for an insidious competitiveness and the emergence of unconscious anxiety. The father's seeming influence over the daughter gives the husband a sense of incomplete possession, and we have a dim occurrence of oedipus recidivus. The husband's mother, on the other hand, has to have a singular maturity to accept into the family a daughter who has married "mother's son." The conflict between mother-in-law and daughter-in-law for possession of the son, and its parallel of the daughter-father complex, becomes a power struggle of many dimensions; and its sequelae are not infrequently encountered as symptoms in the physician's office.

There is, of course, the other side of the coin. There are instances in which the young man who woos a girl meets her mother and marries her instead; and sometimes the young wife discovers in her marriage an affinity between her husband and her mother. The mother-in-law may reawaken positive feelings in the son-in-law reminiscent of those he had toward his own mother. Such feelings may come close to awareness and bring with them an anxiety that is dissipated in surface reactions of hostility and revulsion. Or the mother-in-law may find herself possessive of the son-in-law, unconsciously in rivalry and competition with her daughter.

Many more observations may be made on the wide range and infinite variety of marriage behavior to add support to our thesis that early child-parent relationships remain within the individual throughout his life. Although these relationships are modified as he reaches social maturity the earliest shapings of character will sooner or later inevitably reassert themselves symptomatically in marriage in one way or another. Marriage is an arrangement for living together, and one may say that the domestication of the child is an informal living arrangement of the same order. In later life the formal ritual of marriage is only one marker designating a point along the course of a marital career.

Chapter 5

The Meanings of Love

PHILIP Q. ROCHE, M.D.

IN THE preceding chapter attention was directed to the non-material communication "secreted" by each individual as his symbolic environment, the principle of mind-body, unity, and to the viewpoint that the individual's symbolic environment has its genesis in and a continuity with early formative experience. Some of the problems of marriage were considered in the light of these propositions. A further but limited inquiry into love life will now be attempted, but before doing so we must reach agreement on some conditional issues and impose an emotional preparation upon ourselves in order to lift the veil of that seemingly ineffable part of man's symbolic environment called love.

Many have despaired because love has become a subject of scientific inquiry. Some say that love is a sacred precinct accessible only to poets. Others say that if love is placed under the scrutiny of science, it will be shorn of its enchantment and beauty and reduced to what the moralist Chamfort called it: "Nothing but the contact of two epiderms and the exchange of two pale fantasies." These objections invite endless controversy, since the language in which they are framed suggests that love is something identifiable, something elemental, having dimensions and boundaries. We speak of having love and giving it, or taking it back; of falling in and out of it, losing it, and making it. It becomes visible in the light of one person's eyes and audible in the murmurings of another. It accompanies us from the cradle to the grave. The language used to describe love is explicit of something akin to a magic fluid or stuff, like the *mana* of the Polynesians. In our own symbolic world it occupies a pre-eminent place if for no other reason than that it is incessantly talked and sung about. Denis de Rougemont,[1] in commenting on what one could regard as the saponification of love, says: "No period has spoken more of love, and at the same time exacted so little of it."

The relentless pursuit of the symbol and appearances of love has found its fullest development in contemporary culture. It is a love in quest of an *object* to the neglect of the *function*. Erich Fromm speaks of this feature of our culture:

Our whole culture is based on the appetite for buying, on the idea of a mutually favorable exchange. Modern man's happiness consists in the thrill of looking at the shop windows, and in buying all that he can afford to buy, either for cash or on install-ments. He (or she) looks at people in a similar way. For the man

[1] Denis de Rougemont, *The Devil's Share*, (An Essay on the Diabolic in Modern Society), Meridian Books, New York, 1956, p. 159.

"The Devil has made us give the name of 'love' to a vague contagious obsession whose source in the modern era was romantic literature, and of which novels and films are the distributing agents. This obsession had become the great concern of our civilization in time of peace—the religion of those who no longer want religion. Its sway has extended over the most incongruous realms from literary mysticism to the subway billboards. You cannot take two steps in any city without finding some allusion to it. It reigns over the enormous film industry, over publishing, the book trade, over the sale of perfumes, over the activity of millions of lawyers and doctors, over the illustrated magazines, over all the fashion trades. And over much more besides! For it has modified our whole scale of values. The extravagant over-estimation of love—I mean, of course, that form of obsession which resembles true love as the city of Lyon does a lion—has in our epoch progressively contracted the meaning of and the respect for moral behavior, for sacrifice in the common good, for hard, virile vir-tues. Individual happiness has become our fetish: this is the sign of de-cadence of a civilization."

an attractive girl—and for the woman an attractive man—are the prizes they are after. "Attractive" usually means a nice package of qualities which are popular and sought after on the personality market. What specifically makes a person attractive depends on the fashion of the time, physically as well as mentally. During the twenties, a drinking and smoking girl, tough and sexy, was attractive; today the fashion demands more domesticity and coyness. At the end of the nineteenth and the beginning of this century, a man had to be aggressive and ambitious—today he has to be social and tolerant—in order to be an attractive "package." At any rate, the sense of falling in love develops usually only with regard to such human commodities as are within reach of one's own possibilities for exchange. I am out for a bargain; the object should be desirable from the standpoint of its social value, and at the same time should want me, considering my overt and hidden assets and potentialities. Two persons thus fall in love when they feel they have found the best object available on the market, considering the limitations of their own exchange values. Often, as in buying real estate, the hidden potentialities which can be developed play a considerable role in this bargain. In a culture in which the marketing orientation prevails, and in which material success is the outstanding value, there is little reason to be surprised that human love relations follow the same pattern of exchange which governs the commodity and the labor market.[2]

So far we have conveyed little about love itself; we have only used a word which is one of the most commonplace four-letter English words and one of the most overworked. What can be said of its conventional definition? The word love is derived from the Sanskrit *lubhyati*, meaning "he desires." Webster defines love as a "feeling of strong personal attachment induced by sympathic understanding, or by ties of kinship; ardent affection." Or we may turn to the twelfth century and read in Andreas Capellanus that "Love is a certain inborn suffering derived from sight of an excessive meditation upon the beauty of the opposite sex, which causes each one to wish above all

[2] Erich Fromm, "The Art of Loving," Harper & Brothers, New York, 1956, pp. 3–4.

things the embraces of the other and by common desire to carry out all of love's precepts in each other's embrace." [3] Thus Webster tells us that love is a feeling, Capellanus says that it is an inborn suffering, and Chamfort that it is something tactile and pale.

These definitions do not bring us close enough to actual experience. They are statements that merely link love to other words which tell us little more than the common usage of the word defined. Here we can be reminded of the error that to define something verbally is necessarily to know and understand it. If we are to share experiences, we cannot rely on this kind of definition as a basis for agreement. Agreement is possible only if we employ operational definitions, that is, definitions that will relate words to human experience. We must pay less attention to the talk about love and more to what people do about it, how they actually behave, both consciously and unconsciously. From such observations some inferences of meaning can be drawn.

We may begin with the general observation that human beings appear to behave as if within them there exists forces or drives tending to bring them together in communal interdependence. These drives can be placed in the frame referred to in the preceding chapter as the biological capacity for genital union with the opposite sex and as the social capacity for anxiety-free nongenital love relationships. Together these two capacities are descriptive of human love life in all of its dimensions.

We speak in terms of a dynamic force within ourselves. This force is a common source of energy for both constructive and destructive behavior, for both loving and hating. Observe how easily love is turned into hate and how close both are to the instinctual life of the individual. Hate is closer to the unlearned animal responses of the primitive, closer to what is reflexive in

[3] J. J. Parry, *The Art of Courtly Love*, Columbia University Press, New York, 1941; from *The Portable Medieval Reader*, Viking Press, New York, 1955.

the earliest adaptation of the infant and child. Our child-rearing system is devoted to the domestication of this instinctual force; our aim is to modify its purely reflexive character by introducing feed-back control circuits into the reflex arc. These control circuits not only postpone responses but also allow for the introduction and expression of secondary alternate responses which bring new values in the form of social rewards. The measure of this socialization is a measure of the constructive social life which is centered around marriage. In substance we are saying that at best the capacity for loving is potential. We are born to love but cannot do so until we learn to do so. This learning to love is inextricably bound up with the moral life formalized in our legal and religious institutions. Rollo May [4] points out that the real problem in our day for people is the preparation to love, that is, learning to be able to love:

In the first place, it should be noted that love is actually a relatively rare phenomenon in our society. As everyone knows there are a million and one kinds of relationships which are *called* love: we do not need to list all of the confusions of "love" with sentimental impulses and every kind of oedipal and "back to mother's arms" motives as they appear in the romantic songs and the movies. . . . Our society is the heir to four centuries of competitive individualism, with power over others as a dominant motivation; and our particular generation is the heir of a good deal of anxiety, isolation and personal emptiness. This is scarcely good preparation for learning how to love.

May warns us against sliding into a mushy sentimentality that "love will solve all." In our marketplace orientation

we use love for buying and selling. One illustration of this is in the fact that many parents expect the child to love them as a repayment for their taking care of him. To be sure, a child will learn to pretend to certain acts of love if the parents insist on it; but sooner or later it turns out that a love demanded as a payment is no love at all.

[4] Rollo May, *Man's Search for Himself*, W. W. Norton & Co., New York, 1953.

Sorokin [5] comes near to our operational meaning of love when he refers to it "as a dynamic force effectively transfiguring individuals, ennobling social institutions, inspiring culture and making the whole world a warm, friendly, and beautiful cosmos." Yet in this definition of love we do not escape the notion that love is a force existing in the world outside of ourselves, something like the air we breathe. The definition refers to something transitive and taking place, but it evades the fact that the dynamic force in question is within ourselves. Outside of ourselves it exists only in the communication of our symbolic environment, in the manner of doing, rather than in the substance itself. It is not an element outside of ourselves to which we are passively submissive; on the contrary, it is a potential within ourselves expended in external relationships with people and things.[6]

The formalization of love embraces the concepts of honor, courage, fidelity, and other aesthetic and ethical values that are a part of our symbolic environment. Society's concern here is twofold: the extent to which our child-rearing system makes possible the individual's full potential for loving, and the extent to which the deficit in capacity for loving is obscured, if not substituted for by its formalization, the extent to which *form* gives substance. The physician or counselor may often detect a deficit in the symptoms of his patient, and such symptoms are by no means confined to the clinic. In the wider view of love life, we may outline a general symptomatology related to our child-rearing system and to the formalization of love. Children

---

[5] Pitirim A. Sorokin, *Altruistic Love*, Beacon Press, Boston, 1950.

[6] Erich Fromm, *op. cit.*, p. 21. Erich Fromm speaks of this love potential as the answer to the problem of human existence as a ligating force in life beyond the exclusive erotic love of two people who feel no love for anyone else beyond an egoism *a deux*. This potential insures "union under the condition of preserving one's integrity . . . an active power in man; a power which breaks through the walls which separate man from his fellow man, which unites him with others; love makes him overcome the fence of isolation and separateness . . ."

who fail to learn to love because they have been taught to love
by precept only will in later life lean heavily on the formalization of love. For them, love will be pursued in symbol and symptom rather than in deed. In A. B. Johnson's [7] phrase, they will
"deem the identity a hidden property of nature, while it is
only a property of language." It is through this concept that
our inquiry into the meaning of love can be pursued.

The general symptomatology of love may be regarded as the
manifestations of behavior which express conflict between loving
and hating, between the potential for loving and the residue of
unmodified instinctual drives. This conflict is called *ambivalence*
and may exist on all levels of psychic operation, unconscious or
conscious. Ambivalence may be observed in that most remarkable
form of behavior which communicates simultaneously both loving
and hating; for example in killing a loved one with kindness
or in some compulsive lovers in whom hostility lies behind a
façade of philanthropy. Meerloo [8] remarks that "At the one extreme love is liberation from the purely instinctual drive—it
may be the highest form of sublimation; at the other, possession
by the drive itself, often leading to murder and self-destruction."

Love is a phenomenon of civilized society, and has made a
relatively recent appearance in the history of mankind. It is
said that it has come into its own only with leisure and luxury.
The love stories of early folklore belong to idealization, romance,
and unreality; realistic love stories are hardly more than a hundred years old. In antiquity love was probably erotic for the
most part. Among the Greeks it was regarded as a "mania"
with which a person was afflicted because of the caprice and
malevolence of the gods. The notion of one's wife being closest
to one is relatively modern and accepted by only a comparatively

[7] A. B. Johnson, "The Individuality of Things and the Generality of
Language," Utica, William Williams, 1832, After Irving J. Lee, *The Language of Wisdom and Folly,* Harper and Brothers, New York, 1949, p. 191.
[8] J. A. M. Meerloo, *Two Faces of Man,* International Universities Press,
New York, 1954.

small part of the human race. The concept of love has been associated with the status of women. Trevelyan remarks that with the educated medieval man and woman "marriage was one relation of life, love another . . . love might indeed chance to grow out of marriage as doubtless it often did." [9]

Courtly love was conceived in the eleventh century and was formalized in the contemporary troubadour poetry. It was modeled on the service of love which a feudal vassal owed his lord. Medieval sex mores conjoined two contradictory ideas about women: women were evil and dangerous, to be shunned; women were lovely and adorable, to be revered and worshiped. Out of the amalgam of these two ideas flowed a hypocritical eroticism. In feudal society marriage had little or nothing to do with love. All matches were those of interest. And "love was not conceived of as existing in the marriage state, but outside the bonds of matrimony." [10] Trevelyan further remarks that "among the poor, it is probable that marriage choice had always been less dogged by mercenary motives. Probably the pattern set by 'good society' was followed on a smaller scale by the poor." The gift of the medieval poets to the Western world was a new concept of the love of man and woman as a spiritual thing, a concept unknown to the ancients or to the early church. Trevelyan remarks that in England a gradual change occurred in which the element of love in the marriage became more important than the mercenary element, which has culminated in what we observe today of the free choice of love being acceptable as a basis of marriage. In our times, as Sumner [11] says, it is probably true that matrimony, like conversation, is too readily identified with ritual. This is to say that what is said in the ceremony no longer has much importance; no one pays much attention to it. On the other hand love demands altruism in conjugal affection, good

[9] G. M. Trevelyan, *English Social History*, Longmans Green & Co., New York, 1942, pp. 64–66.

[10] C. S. Lewis, *Allegory of Love*, London, 1936 (Trevelyan).

[11] Wm. G. Sumner, *Folkways*, Ginn & Co., Boston, 1940, p. 374.

sense, a spirit of accommodation, and the maturity of each partner.

J. A. M. Meerloo's [12] book *Conversation and Communication* contains an instructive chapter, "The Word Tyrannizes Us," in which is demonstrated the semantic confusion of the expression "I love you," a statement that occupies a large part of our symbolic environment. Meerloo states:

Sometimes it means: *I desire you* or *I want you sexually.* It may mean: *I hope you love me* or *I hope that I will be able to love you.* Often it means: *It may be that a love relationship can develop between us* or even *I hate you.* Often it is a wish for emotional exchange: *I want your admiration in exchange for mine* or *I give my love in exchange for some passion* or *I want to feel cozy and at home with you* or *I admire some of your qualities.* A declaration of love is mostly a request: *I desire you* or *I want you to gratify me* or *I want your protection* or *I want to be intimate with you* or *I want to exploit your loveliness.*

Sometimes it is the need for security and tenderness, for parental treatment. It may mean: *My self-love goes out to you.* But it may also express submissiveness: *Please take me as I am* or *I feel guilty about you, I want through you, to correct the mistakes I have made in human relations.* It may be self-sacrifice and a masochistic wish for dependency. However, it may also be a full affirmation of the other, taking the responsibility for mutual exchange of feelings. It may be a weak feeling of friendliness, it may be the scarcely even whispered expression of ecstasy. "I love you," wish, desire, submission, conquest; it is never the word itself that tells the real meaning here.

It is evident from these statements that the word love belongs to that category of terms that are multiordinal and as such have no fixed meaning. For those who bring their symptoms of love life to our scrutiny, it is not enough merely to ponder the semantics of the word love; we should discern from its context the underlying meaning of love, less from what the person says

[12] J. A. M. Meerloo, *Conversation and Communication*, International Universities Press, New York, 1952, p. 83.

than from what he does in his love life. With some grasp of its meaning for him, we may be able to effect some change in the individual. How can the physician or counselor structure his analysis and draw inferences from his data? Philip Solomon set himself to answer this question in his article "Love: A Clinical Definition." [13] He systematizes the concept of love utilizable for clinical application in a frame of dimensional analyses in terms of the degree of abstraction of the love object, that is, primary *one-dimensional* self-love, *two-dimensional* love involving unconscious projection of the self externally, *three-dimensional* love as romantic love for one's ideal self, and *four-dimensional* love as mature love striving toward an eventual ideal.

It is likely that in a professional experience with the symptomatology of love, the physician or counselor will note the preponderance of the one- and two-dimensional love, with their consequent dislocations in marriage. These types of love can be reconciled with Freud's original observation of two types of love: *narcissistic* and *dependent*. In the first, the mechanism of projection of the self onto someone else bears an analogy to what one discovers of oneself mirrored in another. Love of this type is exaggerated in homosexual ties, in which the object is a loved facsimile of oneself. In like manner some parents see an extension of themselves in their children. In these dimensions of heterosexual love a man finds in his spouse his own feminine qualities, unconscious to himself, and his wife finds in her husband her unconscious masculine qualities.

Dependent love moves closer to the external love object in the sense that the love object becomes the source of fulfillment of the lover's own bodily and mental needs. One does not have to search far in dependent love relationships to uncover in the loved one a displaced surrogate for a parent, commonly the mother with whom there persists an invisible umbilical tie.

[13] Philip Solomon, "Love: A Clinical Definition," *New England Journal of Medicine*, 252: 345–351, March 3, 1955.

Dependent love is often displaced to brother, sister, or near relative, and later displaced to unrelated persons. An unconscious linkage sometimes apparent to the outside observer animates both narcissistic and dependent love.

In the previous chapter, "Early Life Experience and Marriage," several configurations of symptomatic love life in the adult were discussed in the light of childhood experience. A few more configurations of clinical significance may be mentioned here to illustrate the meanings of love. An impedance of the child's love for the parents will find its way eventually into later love choice. Great literature abounds in the stories of lovers unable to fall in love except with someone already married, husband and wife snatchers, and in stories of those lovers who require obstacles in the path of love, who find a way to be hindered; of others who cannot love without having love shrouded in mystery and secrecy; of those whose love is obviously a translation of the rescue fantasy in which the knight rescues the distressed maiden from the monster. In some instances the boy unconsciously despises his mother for preferring the father, and all subsequent women are held in low esteem. In such symptomatic love situations, we may find that the love object has a medieval aspect: an attractive inferior woman, behind whom broods the image of the prostitute, is placed against the other image of the highly respected woman for whom there is no attraction. This is the ancient oedipal dichotomy of sacred and profane. The dichotomy may find its way into the consultant's office: a husband has ill-defined symptoms arising from his dilemma of having married a woman whom he highly esteems but with whom he can find no libidinal fulfillment. The same thing may also happen to women. Two kinds of men are loved by some women: a physically inferior man who arouses sympathy and tenderness and a morally and socially inferior man who arouses sexual desire and is associated with a need for clandestine relationships. The writer once conferred with a woman who had knowingly married a chronic alcoholic and who had led a life of unremitting disappointment and humiliation about which she bitterly complained. It was suggested that separation from her husband would be a remedy for her life of despair. With unconcealed umbrage she refused even to consider such a move. When asked why, she replied: "Because I love him." The physician may discern in his male patient's symptoms the reflections of a latent combination of prostitute and rescue fantasy—in this case the man's need to lead a fallen woman to a better life; conversely, we see the need of some women to try to rehabilitate a drunkard, ne'er-do-well, or criminal.

In writing of "The Enigma of the Tenderness in Love," Bergler[14] states: "For only when we understand the mysterious mechanism of love and tenderness can we understand the distortions of love with which we are so often confronted in the persons seeking divorce, or can we understand why his marriage has failed." Bergler explicates eight outward signs of tender love which every healthy person is capable of experiencing; those incapable he regards as physically ill, so-called neurotics. The eight signs are:

1. *Subjective feeling of happiness.* Bergler states that the lover finds himself in a state of manic elation. This is close to the classic dictum, *amantes amentes,* lovers are lunatics.

2. *Self-torture.* The lover's happiness is not unalloyed; with it comes doubt and the inevitable anxiety that flows out of his unconscious ambivalence and distrust of his private world, himself, and persons and things. "It's too good to last."

3. *Overvaluation of the loved object.* What the lover apperceives in the loved one is an image of his own projected self-love. Gertrude Stein put it so: "The loveliness is in the you that is in me."

4. *Undervaluation of reality.* This is implied in the overvaluation of the loved object and is reminiscent of the revival of long-buried infantile delusions.

[14] Edmund Bergler, *Unhappy Marriage and Divorce,* International Universities Press, New York, 1946, p. 15 et seq., p. 30.

5. *Exclusiveness*. Bergler avers: "The exclusive interest of the lover for the love object is explained by his boundless self-love."

6. *Psychic dependence on the love object*. This is an analogue of exclusiveness comprehensible in the light of the mechanism whereby the lover is bathed in the ecstatic radiations of his projected self, achieved as "an orgy of self-love without the slightest feeling of guilt. The paradisiacal infantile delusions of grandeur seem to be realized."

7. *Sentimental behavior*. The lover has enshrined himself in the love object, and sentimental behavior appears to be a kind of self-worship.

8. *Predominance of fantasy*. Bergler contends that the exfoliation of fantasy, set in relation to mundane reality, supports the concept that projection accounts for the phenomenon of love. He says: "Happy love means that the central infantile wish fantasy has been realized." The lover has reanimated an old hunger to be fondled, praised, and valued by his parents.

In sum, according to Bergler, the happiness of love is a psychic state in which there appears to be achieved a materialization of three infantile wish fantasies: "(1) the paradisiacal state of childhood omnipotence and of early infantile delusions of grandeur, (2) the belief my parents love me tenderly, and (3) the belief my parents permit my behavior, approve it, and I need therefore feel no guilt." The physician or counselor has in the behavior reflected by these elements the clinical phenomenon of manic elation of the lover.

In considering the signs of tender love, the physician or counselor might be disposed to regard them as pathological. However, we are dealing with a kind of behavior that is "normal" in our culture, in fact, entirely within the range of conventions that are taken as a matter of course. Behavior that is taken as a matter of course tends to be surrounded by impediments to objective analysis, and there seems to be an uncommon threat implied in the examination of the irrational aspects of conventional behavior. However, our concern is not that these irrational aspects of love be deplored but rather that so many of the people we work with are apparently incapable of anxiety-free love at all, that so much of "love" is in fact a pseudo affect and anchored in the unresolved narcissistic infantile fantasy life at the expense of creative living. It may be that in contriving the perpetuation of the species, nature is concerned only with the goal and cares naught for the means. Even if in our view of the order of the world we come to regard the behavior of falling in love as a kind of psychosis, we nevertheless regard it as something quite human and meaningful and not in a pejorative sense. Love is not a biological necessity for the perpetuation of the species; but it is a necessity in the social life of man.

The counselor or physician will meet with many failures of love which he may view in the light of our recently acquired psychological understanding of the workings of mental life. He will observe people in pairs who are unceasingly pursuing in each other the hoped-for fulfillment of an ancient, infantile romance, veneered by the language of conventional love; these loves are actually cases of clinical neuroses and are filled with compulsive jealousy, infidelity, ambition, revenge, and self-destructiveness, not to mention neurotic behavior which is transmitted to the children of such pairings.

In this chapter we have made a wary approach to a precious subject. The phenomenon of love has been examined in the context of the physician's role as a reliever of human suffering, and has been delineated with the purpose of creating an awareness that love life is inextricably bound with physical welfare. The physician and counselor can achieve a fuller service in their calling if they view the people who come to them for help in the totality of physiological and psychic behavior lived out in the medium of their symbolic environment.

Chapter 6

Family Tension and Its Effect on Children

FREDERICK H. ALLEN, M.D.

THE relationship between man and wife has an inevitable effect upon the behavior patterns of their children. Any discussion of conflict and tension between spouses must consider the supporting roles of the mother and father in helping the child find his place in a world into which he has been precipitated. With so little organization around what he really is within himself, the child needs the guidance and direction of parental figures to discover that he can ultimately be a separate and unique individual. For, after all, the world into which the child comes is, for him, largely a prefabricated one.

In the early life of the child we are dealing with two sets of factors. We are concerned not only with what he has been born *with,* in terms of biological equipment and physical endowment, but what he has been born *into.* Before he can discover that he is a person in his own right, separate and apart from everyone else, his parents must help him discover what he can begin to do for himself to sustain his own life and give meaning to it as he grows and becomes, in the end, a confident and mature person. The fact that the child enters life with such an ill-formed ego, that he moves slowly out of the dependency of that early period, means that he is highly vulnerable to circumstances that impinge upon him at the beginning of life.

In this discussion, I want to give a few examples of the different types of marital tension that are reflected in the quality of development and disturbance that we meet in children. One of the first places a child begins to feel the effect of underlying tension is in the feeding experience as illustrated in the following two cases.

A mother sought help for her daughter when the girl was about ten years old. She had developed in a very withdrawn way, was, characteristically, the lone-wolf type, showing little connection with her family in any feeling, emotional sense. She shared almost nothing of what she did or felt and seemed to operate apart from rather than in relation to the other members of her family. In getting at the background of this case, the mother began to reveal the story of her motherhood. This was her first baby. She described her reaction to the first feeding experience as a feeling of intense revulsion. Here was a child of her own creation, here was what she had produced out of herself, and in that sudden awareness of feeling repelled, there dawned upon the young wife her lack of readiness for becoming a parent.

The child was a symbol of a difficult life. Her marriage was fraught with a great deal of tension because she had not been well received into her husband's family, her status being one of an intruder—she had taken a son away from a devoted mother. When the baby came along—and she was a wanted child, at least as far as the mother was aware—there crowded into that earliest feeding experience the sudden feeling that she could have very little to do with the child. For four or five months she had to be fed by a nurse. When, at the age of a year or so, the mother began to have a longing to have some connection with the child, there had been built up a barrier which was to become greater as the years rolled on.

The foregoing is an example of a defense set up in a youngster in the period of greatest vulnerability. It is during the first year that there is normally a slow awakening on the part of the child to being something in himself and to being able to take from the parent that which he needs for his survival and development. In this case, one finds tension in the parent putting a kind of road block into the very early development of the child. As the mother really began to try to find her place in the life of the child, she found that the defenses that had gradually been building up behind the road block were such as to be very difficult to break down.

A second example is of a mother who sought help for her son because of an almost compulsive pattern of delinquency. The boy seemed to be a past master at leaving a train of irritations behind him and getting everyone upset because of things he was doing to his teachers in school, his classmates, and to people in the neighborhood. The mother was baffled. Why should her boy be this way? One or two interviews with her revealed that she had been quite ambitious for a career of her own. In becoming pregnant she discovered that it was necessary to relinquish many of the things she had set her heart upon. She felt deeply frustrated. Nevertheless, during her pregnancy, she made up her mind in a determined and highly intellectual way that she was going to be the perfect mother. She was going to have a child who would be a credit to her and to everyone. The ideal of what she was going to be, and what the child was going to be, was built up during a prenatal period fraught with tension and uncertainty. The baby offered a vehicle with which to atone for all the deep feelings of frustration for having to give up her own life in order to marry and become a wife and then having to give up more of it in order to become a mother.

The birth period was made more difficult by the father's being away at the time, leaving her to carry the entire experience by herself and thus increasing her feeling of hostility toward being married in the first place and toward the husband who was not there to support her during a trying time. When the child was born, the anxious tension of the mother immediately began to get into the feeding and other early experiences with the child, who in turn became fretful and in his crying and squalling was far from the ideal the mother had built up in her dreams. This led to a more determined effort that this child of her creation should, by his perfection, compensate for her basic feeling of hostility. As a result, an apparently alert and vigorous child began to react negatively toward all the efforts directed to make him something the parent wanted him to be.

At the age of four, the boy took to running away into the neighborhood. He had an amazing capacity, even at that age, of involving everybody. When the police picked him up he would give them a story about how badly he was treated at home, describing a terribly drab situation of not getting enough to eat and other deprivations. Thus he would immediately get everybody drawn over on his side and feeling what terrible parents he had. Naturally, this only further infuriated the mother and made it imperative that she take steps to gain hold of a situation over which she was rapidly losing control. A sequence of events followed in which the boy thought that all the world was against him and saw to it by his behavior that they *were* against him. Because everyone seemed to be ganged up against him, it seemed natural to retaliate. In time he began to feel that he had little to do with his own actions. A series of projections were set in motion, with the school blaming the parents for having a bad child, the boy blaming the parents for not loving him, and the mother blaming the boy for being inherently and constitutionally bad.

One of the more prevalent types of tension situations occurs in what might be called the paradoxical type of stimulation. To some degree this was true in the cases already cited, where we see that the parent has an ambivalent quality of loving the child while at the same time repelling him. The paradoxical type of stimulation results when the man and wife are not together on their feeling of responsibility and on their sense of values as to what a child is or what he can become. Most frequently encountered is the situation of an overindulgent parent—it can be either parent—with the other reacting by becoming overly strict and severe. Young children are remarkably sensitive to these shifts in attitude. Theirs is not an awareness that one can spell out in definite words or in an intellectual formulation. In any event the marital tension is felt by the child, and he may respond with certain physical symptoms. Thus when a child is faced with these paradoxical types of stimulation, confusion results. Instead of complementing each other, the parental roles are working at cross-purposes, and the child reflects this lack of unity in his behavior.

One of the most baffling situations we encounter arises out of serious physical illness in infancy. I recall a case in which a mother was constantly concerned and distressed about whether her five-year-old boy could get along without her. She felt that the boy was incapable of having experiences of his own. In the background of this case one can get a good deal of psychological understanding both of the mother's anxiety and the child's struggle against anything that separates him from his mother.

In this instance, the child had been seriously ill during the first year of life, and the mother had been told by the attending physicians that the child could not possibly have lived had it not been for her constant care. Here was a mother who was giving wholly and fully of herself; her attentions to the child were not based on underlying hostile or rejecting attitudes, for she continued her ministrations for five years, feeling the risk that was involved in anything the boy did when apart from her. Hence comes the block in the differentiating process which is present in the normal growth period. It is in these earliest years that the child begins to carve, out of all that the parent gives, a feeling of being something within himself which he can sustain without the constant attention, direction, and giving that the parent provides. Gradually the mother developed a fear that the child was not alert. She noticed, too, that he seemed to lack aggressive qualities; he seemed afraid of every new experience. Slowly, she began to awaken to the fact that she was finding the child a burden. And as she began to try to put some reality into the child's life, she found him responding in an inert fashion. It was only then that the mother realized that the child was a person in his own right and not just a product of her own will and all she had given.

Other types of tension enter the picture in the case of husbands and wives who feel that they have failed in their own lives. Here we get pressure to recapture in the child those deficits and frustrations that have characterized the parents' own life journey. The type of emotional damage that can accrue to a child when he has to become the symbol of a success that has far more meaning to another person than to himself should be apparent. How many times do we find these children in their later childhood and adolescence developing negative attitudes toward the very things they are capable of achieving?

I recall a boy I once saw who was brilliantly talented along musical lines. His mother had wanted to be a musician, but while she had a great deal of appreciation for music she did not have in her development the skill for becoming one. As her child began to develop these skills, the mother saw the opportunity to fulfill her own hopes. At the age of thirteen, the boy, who had devoted a great deal of time to becoming what his mother wanted, began to wake up to the fact that he had very little life of his own. He noticed that while he was practicing the piano other boys were out playing football and doing other things that were normal for boys of that age. He began to feel a certain barrenness within himself and soon he began to react by becoming very negative to those very qualities he had but could not really experience as his own because they were synthetically created.

His parents were confused. "Why is our boy who is so capable now refusing to do any of the things he previously did?" they asked. "Why is he even rebelling against school?" The boy himself was raising these questions. "Why is it I suddenly want to throw the whole thing overboard? Why is it I just want to kick over the traces? To tell my music teacher to go to hell?" He felt guilty because he was trying to destroy something in himself. During our interviews he revealed that he wanted to be something other than the apple of his mother's eye. He wanted to be something within himself, and the destructive and negative way seemed to be the only course open to him.

Our next case concerns a divorcee who spent much of her time making her daughter feel that the father was a louse. The mother herself was a ne'er-do-well and irresponsible sort of a person who gave her daughter little emotional nourishment. At sixteen, the girl described a fascinating dilemma. She told how all through the time of growing up, feeling the effort of her mother to get her to feel the way she did, she found herself actually doing exactly the opposite. Now, in adolescence, as she began to feel something really positive in herself toward her father, she raised this question: "Do I really feel this way or is it because it is the opposite of what my mother has tried to make me feel?"

The confusion this girl experienced led her to feel that status in life could be gained only through knowing everything about everybody and anything. Hence at the age of sixteen she knew all about sexual behavior, all about homosexuality. She was burdened with knowledge that she herself said a woman should not have, at least until she is older and knows what to do with it—all to achieve status. All her experiences had been so negatively charged, they seemed almost to destroy that quality in herself over which she could not feel any sense of ownership.

It is likely that the forms of behavior most fraught with tension and anxiety involve the field of sex. Many parents begin to show concern when they see a certain sexual awakening in the child.

They notice some of the early explorations of the child when he begins to discover pleasure in his body and make of it a battle-ground. I recall a woman who came in greatly troubled about the fact that her seven-year-old daughter was constantly doing "it," "it" referring to "masturbation," a bad word she could not include in her vocabulary. Her approach was as roundabout as her ways of trying to deal with the situation. She was afraid to come directly to the point. Her little girl, on the other hand, was apparently quite an up and coming little piece of machinery with a very real will of her own. In desperation, one day, the mother said: "Why do you keep on doing *it?*" The little girl looked her straight in the eye and replied: "Because I want to." This was probably about as good an answer as any child could have given. Her "wanting," though, was negatively charged, being shot through with the anxiety and tension of a parent who could not come through and say "I want you to cut it out!" When the mother was able to see how some of these things were really the product of her own great anxiety and lack of understanding of what constitutes a child, the tension began to diminish. The child's self-stimulation was no longer a favorable battleground and the behavior began to disappear.

Tensions get built up sometimes around large things and sometimes around small ones. A mother came to me some years ago and talked in the most serious fashion about how worried she was because her child was sucking her thumb. We had a half-hour interview, and I don't particularly remember the content except that she was very morose, as though the world were falling to pieces because the child was sucking her thumb. I must have taken part in the interview because six months later she came to me and said: "Do you remember what was the most important thing you did during that interview?" I was curious because I hadn't thought I had done anything especially important. "Well," she said, "you smiled."

Now if I smiled I wasn't smiling by way of belittlement or

even as an attempt to alleviate the mother's intense seriousness. Yet that was what had relieved her tension. It was that smile that began to restore to the mother a sense of balance which enabled her to deal with the situation for what it was rather than with all the anxious anticipations that were making it something totally different. Thus in the early life of the child tensions sometimes begin to build up around small things and produce distorted values. We can help parents obtain perspective. The ability to see things in proportion makes it possible for them to see the child not as a symbol of all the frustrations and difficulties of their own lives but as a new emergent in the life process carrying within itself the potential for real development.

Obviously, I do not subscribe to the fairly widespread notion that parents are an unnecessary evil in a child's life and the quicker they move out the better. That kind of attitude only accentuates the very problems we want to help parents resolve. Adequate parents have a quality that helps the child gain a certain kind of organization within himself that spells health, creative activity, and purpose and that enables him to live through the normal tensions that arise in the life of every child. Parents who are unable to use this quality can be helped to do so during professional service.

Now, paradoxically, sometimes when parents are working too hard to avoid tension, the effort boomerangs. Such parents try to make life pleasant at all costs. Probably because they have had a hard life themselves, they want to give the child every advantage and thereby protect him from those normal pains and anxieties that are a part of every human growth experience. Such a child finds it very difficult to understand the language of discomfort and pain because these experiences are not in his vocabulary. We know that many times, in trying to create a life along too pleasant lines, we introduce a certain degree of unreality. We know that children can bear tension, pain, even tragedy, when supported by parents who are able to bear it with them.

During the war, for instance, the English learned that children were not distorted by their experience of danger and tragedy when they had the backing and confidence of parents who saw it through with them. I think sometimes we get the feeling that children are little pieces of bric-a-brac because they are so vulnerable to certain kinds of tension. Sometimes this leads us to introduce factors of guardedness and overprotection into their lives so that they become unable to take the rough with the smooth. Not only can we live with pain and discomfort, but we can be strengthened by living through the experience.

Tragedies that arise out of tension between man, wife, and child are numerous and extremely difficult to deal with. We see how they begin early in the life of the child. We see the actual application of the old Biblical saying that the sins of one generation are visited on the next. We see how one set of tensions creates other tensions and how these in turn multiply and the vicious cycle is set in motion. The turning point comes with the child's first feeling of being something himself. The parents play the key role in nourishing that first awakening and giving it direction and meaning; for it is out of his feeling of relatedness to the adult figures that the infant's sense of himself develops. It is at this point, too, that the child is most vulnerable. By the same token, this is the time that efforts to help the parents to look through some of their own anxieties are most effective. To begin with they may be relatively slight, but anxieties gradually mount as the child begins to react to them. This stirs more anxiety which provokes more effort to comfort and help the child. It is in these periods, if we understand the importance of parental roles and the great potential they contain for health and illness, that real effort pays the highest dividends.

Chapter 7

Parental Models

LEON J. SAUL, M.D.

PERSONALITY and sexual development are complex, as are early life experiences, marriage, and parenthood, but the principles of child rearing—and when I talk about the child I talk of the marriage, too—seem to me to be relatively simple. Practically these principles may be hard to achieve, as is evident in Dr. Allen's description in the preceding chapter of family tension, but theoretically they are not too difficult. In the first place, I think the motto should be that of the surgeon—*primum non nocere*—the first duty is to do no harm. Parents should be acquainted with the pitfalls of child rearing: overprotection and underprotection, pushing a child into too much responsibility or not letting him take enough, not socializing him enough or socializing him too suddenly, too early, too harshly, or too inconsistently.

The child needs to be socialized, but this can be done by a gradual process which it can accept. It is of the utmost importance to keep good emotional relations with the child. Parents ask: "Is it all right to spank the child, or is it better to scold him, or what shall I do?" The answer depends upon the individual, and I think the touchstone there is whether in the handling of the child, the child still loves the parent. Is it still a good relationship? Is it warm, friendly, easy? If you can socialize the child, handle him, even punish him if necessary (and I question whether punishing children is ever essential and not a symptom of mishandling) and at the same time maintain a basically good human relationship, you have prepared, you have preserved the pattern of good relationships in later life which is the core of a healthy personality.

This result assumes that the training of the child has been favorable to his development. If his training has not been favorable, it can either inhibit or exaggerate parts of the development. For example, though, I do not think that toilet training per se can be singled out as crucial to the child's development in the broader sense—and it is not a one-to-one correlation. However, the period of toilet training is usually the period of *general* training. The parents are apt to be too dominating and too demanding in many ways and to apply these attitudes to toilet training in particular. "You absolutely can't go to school and you can't do this and you can't do that unless you first succeed on the toilet and show that your bowels are all right." Of course this kind of after-breakfast demand belongs to an era that hopefully is past. But the parent who is overly strict about toilet training is not apt to be in other respects open and broad and tolerant and helpful to the child's development. The same domination is likely to appear in his training of all the other phases of the child's social development.

It is interesting how often if you analyze patients—or if you don't analyze them but just listen to their stories—you find people who have the problem of domination and submission. I saw a young man recently whose feeling was that he was unhappy about himself. He was always more or less enraged because he always felt that he had to be a good boy; and he had to be a good boy because that was how he got along. He was; and he did get along. But it bothered him. Why should he be disturbed about it? Because he felt that in his own family the price of getting along was submission. For him, to be good was not to be good as an adult who enjoyed his life but to be submissive to his parents. In the midst of the narrative he said: "It reminds me of one of my very earliest memories when I couldn't have been much over two or three. I remember I was sitting on the potty and I just waited. And the family was interested and they wanted me to do something." He didn't quite remember his own sensation, but in the middle of the interview he brought out this kind of memory.

As a corollary to gradual socialization, the parents should provide a setting of emotional warmth for the child, just as you provide the warmth of the sunshine and good soil for your plants or flowers to grow in. Provide all this, and let the child develop. For instance, if he looks cute, you don't rush over to him and pick him up and start to hug and kiss and cuddle him just because he's adorable. He was doing all right and was happy and cute the way he was, and you don't run in and do something about it, even though you have the impulse to. All of which involves a little understanding of, and object interest in, the child.

Let us look at two brief examples of intensified sensuality of local zones resulting from unthinking use of the child by the parent. A young man's complaint was that he had irresistible impulses to kiss men while riding in trains. In the whole structure of the case there was one fact that emerged strongly: the amount of actual kissing on the mouth that the father had done to the boy when a baby had greatly exaggerated his oral sexuality. We see a similar situation in a patient who came from a different culture. In his culture parents do not inhibit the sexual play of children the way we do. There, little boys play together by getting into a kind of chain, each behind the other, and this fellow had his anal sensations very much stimulated. As in the first case, although psychologically the man grew out of it pretty much, married and had a family and enough masculine pride to make a go of things, there still lurked latent in the background a high degree of anal sensation which was strong enough so that he had homosexual fantasies as well as a tendency to anal masturbation which led to orgasm and so on.

This is a rather typical result when stimulation of a particular area becomes mechanical. From parents who are stimulating to the child's genitals we get nymphomania and satyriasis; and from parents who are afraid of any manifestation of sexuality, we get persons who are greatly inhibited sexually. With these illustrations I want to emphasize that everybody has within himself a residue of all sensations and to show what can happen when the conditioning is not good.

It is essential that the child develop through the unfolding of his nature and potentialities. This nature is to develop from a passive-receptive-dependent organism into a responsive-productive-independent adult, which means growth of the capacity for taking responsibility, being productive, and being able to love and be loved. (See Chapter Three for Dr. Saul's elaboration of this concept.) Every grownup remains a child to some extent. There is no 100 per cent maturity. All work and no play makes Jack a dull boy, you remember. It's a case of enjoying *both* sides of every sensation and situation, the childlike and the mature, in ways that do not harm the person himself or others.

Some mention must be made, too, of the child's need for love which is at the bottom of the great rivalry among children. A child wants to be loved as much as or more than his brother or sister. The brother or sister comes along, and the child fights because he wants to be loved exclusively. These rivalries are inevitable, but they can be handled if the parent is forewarned. If he knows, for instance, that sibling rivalry is a virulent thing, a powerful force that the little ones have to struggle with, then it can be fitted in with the course of development. You cannot stop it by a mere discussion. But you can help it tremendously, even in a child five or six years old, if you discuss the fact of envy and rivalry and wishes for love and keep it in the child's language. We must translate for the child and get across the feeling that we understand these things that all children experience. Sometimes it produces a tremendous effect to say that you have had the same experience: "Oh, I know what a hard time you are having with little Willie, but let me tell you about my experiences with little Annie when I was only four years old."

There is probably a natural competition with the parent of the same sex, but this, too, is only part of growing up unless bad child rearing heightens or distorts it. I think the child grows naturally in the masculine or feminine direction if he or she is simply let alone. The inevitable rivalries and problems in the human relations of the growing child can be handled by a parent who does not have great technical knowledge but does have human interest and the capacity to communicate with the child. The essential point is for the parents to avoid the all too common abuses in child raising.

To develop properly the child needs good models. If he has fairly mature, well-balanced parents with whom to identify, he can stand a great deal of abuse and still turn into a fairly well-balanced adult. If, on the other hand, he has infantile, fixated, regressed, hostile, aggressive, passive-receptive-dependent parents, then he models himself on them. I think that is the practical difficulty in preventing neurosis, psychosis, criminality, and all the other emotional disorders which we believe are the results of faulty child raising. We see these maladjustments as the effects of injurious conditioning treatment of the child during his formative years. But since we have made only a beginning, we can be justifiably optimistic. I am willing to take a stand on preventive psychiatry and say that it is possible in time to produce responsible-productive-independent people.

Chapter 8

Fidelity and Infidelity

M. ROYDEN C. ASTLEY, M.D.

THE word "infidelity" as applied to marriage is generally taken to connote adultery, but in this chapter, although sexual considerations will not be excluded, we shall be discussing a concept of fidelity and infidelity that contains, rather than focuses upon, consideration of sexual infidelities.

The exclusive one-to-one relationship which is presented in our culture as the optimum for marriage is an ideal not frequently realized; but let us hasten to say it is an ideal rooted in the deepest longings of each human being. It is our purpose here to consider how this deep rooting comes about and why in spite of this, attainment of the ideal is so difficult.

Poets and psychologists seem to agree that an adult's sexual activity represents the epitome of his personality: if all goes well in this area, a state of health is reflected; and if there is not a state of health, then in some fashion, sooner or later, the sexual life reflects the illness. For healthy people, the sexual life opens a way in the most gratifying of its intimacies for a kind of obliteration of time and separateness; hence a glance at some of the characteristic reactions and responses involved will perhaps throw some light on the problems surrounding fidelity.

To begin with, the state of falling in love or of being in love does not necessarily have a connection with the mature kind of regard that we think of when we recognize that one healthy adult loves another. A person who has fallen in love tends to idealize and overestimate the loved one, to overlook or minimize aspects which in a different emotional situation he would take very seriously, and to find attractiveness and beauty even in flaws. He is oriented toward his love as if he had discovered the embodiment of ultimate perfection, and he yearns for a means of participation in the excellences he sees. Interests that ordinarily engage his attention are forsaken in favor of those that he supposes, correctly or not, may be of importance to his love, whose modes and standards tend to supplant his own. His self-esteem becomes a matter of his love's opinion; his joy is in acceptance, his despair in rejection. Loved, he is delighted with himself; unnoticed, he is annihilated. Even scorn is better, for that is at least a response.

When the being in love is mutual—"What *do* they see in one another?"—the tendency is for the lovers to communicate not only by small private signs that exclude everyone else and are contrived for one another only, but also by terms of endearment that partake increasingly of the quality of diminutives. Those who eavesdrop may be amused, but no one need be an interloper to know that pet names, baby talk, and a return to childhood expressions are a part of adult love play. Lovers play toward each other a mutual dual role: they behave as parents toward an adored and delightful child, and also as the child who craves and thrives upon the doting of the parent toward whom he looks for strength and inspiration.

This kind of being in love, so characteristic of adolescence, is one of the happiest experiences of life, albeit likely also to be troubled, since fantasy plays so great a role, and since neither the perfect child nor the perfect parent exists. All too often the outcome has the flavor of bitter tragedy; realities assert their claims, and dreams that are truly fond must be reluctantly abandoned.

The childlike quality of being in love offers a clue to the reason for its immensely moving effect: the child who lives on within us—the unconscious—has a claim for uncritical loving and being loved that is never finally paid. This we had once (or wanted), and will always be striving to find again (or at last). The healthy adult, however, has a way of meeting this need from time to time as circumstances make it wise: his sexual life offers him opportunities for loving encounters in which the restraints of adult social life are gradually abandoned by mutual happy consent, and in which the childhood claims can be gratified completely—or as nearly so as is ever possible for human beings; time and separateness are at least momentarily obliterated. For the healthy adult, sexual relationships offer a way of falling in love over and over again.

But what of the between times? The child is notably self-centered and scarcely concerns himself, unless his need for the parent becomes intense, about the interests or welfare of that parent. His capacity for being, as it were, from time to time in love, is great; but his potential for loving is small. He is unable, by and large, to postpone his own gratification in the interest of another, or to seek the other's pleasure or welfare first. He cannot behave as a reliable, responsible, realistic, loving person; these are ways of functioning that he must learn and that are characteristic of the adult—of the good parent.

The adult has to have learned to be able to play two roles if he is to be healthy: he has to be able to be—really *be*—adult as he loves; and he has to be able to be—*really* be—a child as he falls in love or is sexually active. The capacity to enjoy both roles, indeed the desire and need to enjoy both, will be characteristic of him.

Since people differ in their childhood experiences, in their training and the formation of their consciences and ideals, in their capacity for enduring frustration, and in their strength and scope in meeting and dealing with others and with reality, even quite healthy people will differ a great deal from one another. They will have different preferences, tastes, limits, and goals, and even when these are very similar, quantitative differences will appear. In addition, the vicissitudes of reality make different demands, qualitatively and quantitatively, on different people at different times. With so many variables it is scarcely strange that the best of loves become at times disappointing, frustrated, unrewarding, or embittered.

Besides, few of us are healthy in the rather ideal sense in which the word is being used here, so that the tendency to be too soon wearied in well-doing, to be oversensitive, or to mistrust or shrink from trusting is stronger than we like to think. If frank neurosis has played a part in shaping our characters, then so much less are we able to sustain adult love and adult sexuality, and so much more do we feel misunderstood, rejected, belittled, and unfulfilled.

The ideal of marriage in our culture, however, requires constancy in the face of all these difficulties. It asserts that in relation to a single partner a person should be able all his life to fulfil both his roles as adult and as child satisfactorily, or, when one or the other role meets with dissatisfaction, to bear the frustration "for better for worse, for richer for poorer, in sickness and in health, to love and to cherish, till death us do part." The emphasis upon and the yearning for constancy are clearly based in part on the desire deep in the individual to find a loving person who can forever be depended upon not to change, in part on the adult willingness to assume seriously the responsibility for a beloved whose welfare and whose favors will be his exclusive right, and in part on society's need to maintain the health of children via some institution, in this case the family.

Bernard Shaw remarks in *Man and Superman* that "when two people are under the influence of the most violent, most insane, most delusive and most transient of passions, they are required to swear that they will remain in that excited, abnormal, and

exhausting condition continuously until death do them part."
Clearly, no one is required to swear to any such thing, though
Shaw's expostulation does make a point. No one has to swear
that he will be *in* love—only that he will *love*, which is to say
that he will behave like the adult aspect of the ideal lover.
Furthermore, lovers, once they are thoroughly in love, swear
such fealty privately, and though they may boggle a bit at a
public avowal (particularly the men), they object remarkably
little. They plan for fidelity.

Unfortunately, however, as we said above, to be able to love
is not a capacity that necessarily follows from being in love.
It might be asserted that being in love gives one a good start: it
provides a common basis of privately shared experiences of a
precious sort, and a situation in which forbearing and understanding and regard can develop in a particularly propitious
environment. Sexual experiences, if they are part of the picture,
are likely to touch upon very deep-running longings for mutual
pleasure and mutual trust that especially evoke a sense of belonging. If the opportunity for such a happy kind of beginning
should not, however, be set within a background of individual
integrity and responsibility in a mature sense, then as reality
comes more and more to the fore, it is as if the lovers had awak-
ened from a most delightful dream—and on an unusually dreary
Monday. The honeymoon period in most marriages is something
that, once over, can be recaptured from time to time; but without a mutual adult orientation, not only the honeymoon period
but the relationship itself will soon be over—or at best, must be
slowly and painfully replaced with something that at that point
is very difficult to begin to establish.

In such a situation, fidelity in all areas is threatened. From the
most mundane aspects of life, such as cooking, cleaning, the
reasonable sharing of financial responsibility, and ordinary social
decency, to the most abstruse and esoteric physical, emotional,
and intellectual complexities, there will be irritation, dissatisfac-

tion, and the search for another love, if not actively, then by inference. Constancy remains in form at most, and then, likely, mainly in terms of chill and various forms of hatred. In such a case—when immaturity is yoked with immaturity or neurosis with neurosis—treatment or counseling is a real desideratum for both partners; perhaps it should be called a necessity. This is especially true since so often when there is divorce and a second try the pattern is repeated.

In almost every marriage, however, even though it be better based than the tragic picture just described, critical times will come to threaten the relationship. As the man's energies are claimed more and more by the urgencies of his career or job, or as the woman's are taken up in bearing and caring for children, one or the other may suffer pangs of deprivation and the feeling of being rejected or of not mattering. When such a constellation passes the point that exhausts patience and efforts to understand and comply and collaborate, real trouble arises. Then the renewal of mutual delight is elusive and, out of pique, may even be spurned; but the childhood yearnings become increasingly assertive, and a "more understanding" or "more giving" partner is sought. In the very seeking lies the inconstancy or infidelity. The adultery, if it occurs, is only an evidence of a relationship already terribly stressed and torn.

It would be quite impossible to make an exhaustive list of the kinds of situations that serve to strain marital relationships; for, as has been said above, people differ so much in the resources and assets and limitations and liabilities that they bring to *any* relationship that a highly individual response underlies the appearance of signs of stress. On the other hand there are some generalizations, in terms of groupings, that are possible because of statistical frequencies, although a particular one may not be at all applicable in an individual case.

Immaturity. Generally speaking, this refers to underdevelopment in notable degree of facilities for reasonably good management of the business of living in the world, especially with people. The significance of things may be missed for lack of sufficient perceptiveness, thinking may be shallow and superficial, judgment poor, and action ill-advised, ill-timed, or avoided.

In addition, feelings run strong, and behavior may be precipitate, without adequate consideration as to possible outcomes. However much charm an immature person may have, he is likely before long to become more exasperating than rewarding and more demanding than reliable. One might as well be married to a child.

It happens not infrequently that the lack of development is one-sided. A woman may have had everything domestic done for her, so that she brings to her marriage no conception of the amount of energy involved in housekeeping or how the energy must be distributed—in seeing what will need to be done, how it may be done, optimum ways of accomplishing it, and so on. A man, on the other hand, may have no conception of domestic duties himself, and may expect that in some magical way the needs of the house will be taken care of (while he contributes nothing but money) and his wife always free to be with him. The fact of dirty dishes comes as a shock. Now given good sense and a tolerance of frustration, these difficulties can be overcome; but stresses like these can produce strain of such proportions that flight to a fantasied better love looms as a possible alternative to constancy. One can think of scores of examples, perhaps the most famous of which is David Copperfield's Dora.

People in such situations require help in growing up: patience, support, clarification, education (for example referral to cooking school), sometimes persuasion, even chiding. The counselor or therapist toward whom the client consciously or unconsciously looks for sympathy and understanding love in a fashion that is rooted in his childlike orientation (he will try to find what seems missing at home) must really accomplish a kind of rearing. If the client is reasonably healthy, this will not be too difficult, for it always hurts the pride of an adult when he reacts childishly, so that the counselor has a strong ally in the client's desire to feel good about doing an adult job—although the outraged child in him may obscure this fact for some time.

Character Problems. People in this group are the most unpredictable, difficult, fascinating, and rewarding in terms of understanding and of treatment. It is tempting to suggest that the very fact of being a human being means that as regards marriage everyone will have a character problem, for since each member of society is unique, some aspect of his uniqueness is bound to be inadequate for the task of maintaining an excellent one-to-one relationship, and there will inevitably be clashes if each partner always reacts characteristically as he did before the ceremony.

A most pleasant example of this is set down in Richard Aldrich's account of his married life with Gertrude Lawrence, *Mrs. A.* Neither husband nor wife was easily able to differentiate the values of the relationship from the highly invested personal values which, from long, pleased accustomedness, each had brought to the marriage. It was only the great worth, partly realized, partly only glimpsed and sensed, of their relationship to each other that held the two together, while each worked—and worked hard—on the differences in personal values, learning that such values must be assessed again and again, reevaluated, and then discarded, softened, or reinforced; thus it was only because of that work that the marriage could be maintained. Love's labor, of this sort at least, is seldom lost; and in this case, it seems to have added immeasurably to their regard for each other.

We feel that the personal values and standards, conscious and unconscious, which with fair consistency guide and dictate our modes of responding and acting, delineate character. There is implied a tendency to fixity or immutability—a pattern that is more or less set.

Sometimes a character is miserably constructed. Selfish, self-centered, even hateful orientations to the world and people are actually felt to be reasonable and right, or at least justified. Interest in cruelty and suffering may be peculiarly a part of a person's individuality, and he requires their counterparts in his mate. We have only to think of two sorts of marriage to recognize this situation: one in which the woman year after year accepts subjugation, humiliation, and abuse, either emotional or physical, while her yearnings for respect and admiration and tenderness go begging; and the other in which the man is henpecked, subservient, and despised, while his aspirations toward vigorous assumption of responsibility and activity are sabotaged. The forms of marriages such as these may vary from the grossest physical assaultiveness to the subtlest kind of social or personal torture, but always, if they go on for more than a very few years, it may be inferred that a certain compliance is present in the sufferer. However, people do have breaking points, and if worms do not always turn completely, they often turn at least in the direction of someone who seems less harsh and more tender or more accepting and admiring.

By and large, although most people who have trouble in marriage feel terribly mistreated and respond with hostility, such sharply delineated problems as the ones just described, which are based on destructiveness as a goal, are not the most common. Usually it is in the areas of unmet childhood needs for love, receptivity, dependency, and passivity that character problems have their roots. The insistent yearnings are likely to be handled in one of two ways, and generally both are confusedly mixed: either the person expects too much, or he cannot let himself (for reasons of false pride) accept enough. He is angry if not gently and tenderly handled; angry if he's babied. She is angry if much is expected of her and angry if treated as a child.

The difference between people with the problem of simple immaturity and those with a character problem is that the former never knew anything different—have simply still to grow —while the latter seem to have settled, probably out of deep fear of doing anything else, for an ill-designed but characteristic pattern that may be vexedly intricate and involve a number of complex levels. For example, a man's passivity may be in part valued by him because he became convinced that his mother, and women in general, liked docile men better than assertive ones; but it may simultaneously be a valuable defense against being strong like his father, whose strength he regarded as a menace to women and children; and it may further represent a means of placating that same father, with whom he'd like to compete; and, in addition, it may serve as a way of managing a kind of wheedling control, yielding a warped sense of superiority to boot. How can a problem such as this be expressed in terms of fidelity and constancy? Only in fantasy can such a person ever find a lasting love, and even then no one fantasy will serve. The answer is he cannot achieve reasonable comfort without long, careful, skilled treatment; and no marriage can offer this.

Naturally, some character problems are relatively simple, while others are immensely complex and difficult. The reasons for this are themselves difficult to unravel, having to do with the many conflicts and possible resolutions that the individual faces in his movement toward maturity. In the simpler problems, although the tendency to inconstancy and infidelity in marriage may be great, there may also be amazingly happy changes after relatively few interview hours; but this can happen only with knowledgeable and skillful work—or, as everywhere else in life, by some lucky chance that has no connection with disciplined therapy, casework, or counseling.

Neurosis and Psychosis. We cannot discuss here all the ramifications that overt psychic illness may entail in connection with infidelity. To mention one sort of problem: a man who in illness deeply doubts his masculinity and potency may be forced to reassure himself by a series of superficial liaisons with many women. These liaisons have a bogus aspect—they lack even evanescent mutuality and are at an almost masturbatory level. By the same token a woman who has never been fortunate enough to know, really, that she is nice may have to seek re-assurance (which never comes) through promiscuity. When the twistings of fantasy and fear have been altogether too great, hatred and sex may combine to bring about rape, murder, and suicide—a dreadful travesty of the deep need of men and women to love and be loved and a frightful distortion, prompted by fear and rage, of the healthy yearning to love actively and yet find a way to be close and quiet and safe.

We do not wish to imply here that neurosis and psychosis lead in more than a few cases to such violent tragedies. Actually, character disorders are generally based on neurotic conflicts, so the separation of these two headings is somewhat misleading. As we are using the term neurosis here, we imply such illness as shows clear symptomatology: inappropriate and ungovernable fears, compulsions, and obsessions and hysterical anesthesias and paralyses. The sexual life is always disordered to some degree in neurosis. The psychoses evidence a quite open break with reality, often with delusions, hallucinations, or extremely inappropriate attitudes or changes of mood.

It would not be true to say that sufferers from neuroses and psychoses never recover without treatment; but it is not reasonable, either, to expect that they will. Marriage can rarely be sustained by such ill persons, and certainly not without great hardship and long suffering. Psychiatric care is to be sought.

Situational Reactions. Certain events or situations are stressful to all human beings; frank misfortunes—a serious business reverse, for instance, or loss of job, serious illness, especially if prolonged, a child in grave trouble, prolonged separation, as in wartime—are hardships that bring about a longing for relief both from pain and from responsibility. Often, too, the nodal points in life, the new departures, are fraught with mixed feel-

ings. The birth of a first child, for example, while cause for re-
joicing, has many effects beside the easily recognized happy ones.
The interest of the parents must henceforth flow toward the
child as well as toward one another. Fantasies related to priva-
tion, competition, and rivalry may be activated, evidenced perhaps only by anxiety, or covered up by guilt and shame (or
their defenses). In like fashion, promotions, new cars, moves,
increased income, social success, the marriage of children—all
these may evoke discomfort as well as, or along with, pleasure.
Soap opera thrives on such matters.

Any list must include the emotional and physiological changes
of middle life, when questions of self-esteem, self-regard, value,
status, and prestige come so painfully forward to be dealt with
once more. It seems that almost any change can make a person
wonder "Am I really lovable?" and "Am I up to it?" and then
lead him to try to find solutions that will seem to circumvent
the apparent reality that feels so harsh and unyielding.

EVALUATION OF INFIDELITY IN THE
DIAGNOSTIC SITUATION

What has been implied in this discussion is that inconstancy
and infidelity in some degree threaten every marriage and will
occur in most, and if fantasies and dreams are included, then we
might as well say in all. How are we to view this fact, and
particularly how view sexual infidelity—that is, extramarital intercourse or adultery?

To begin with, it looks as if, in infidelity, we may be dealing
with a symptom—an evidence of a disorder—perhaps like overeating. A competent physician presented with overeating would
make a careful differential diagnosis, for he would have in mind
the host of underlying conditions that may prompt excessive
food intake, ranging from dangerous disturbances like severe
diabetes, through foolish and risky habits, to occasional, self-

limiting overindulgence at the annual lodge banquet. In any event, the doctor would individualize the case and arrive at his conclusions via a painstaking history and physical examination, with appropriate tests, all of which would be collated to make a diagnosis and prognosis as well as treatment plan, if indicated.

It does seem that a person who is completely faithful is as rare as one who always eats wisely and with good nutrition in mind. Perhaps both miss something.

It is a pretty dull husband who never responds at all to a flirt; and a woman who never so much as realizes that there are other men in the world scarcely puts a man on his mettle. Conversely, a bland assumption of proprietorship in either partner calls for something to add piquancy to the flavor of the relationship. The child does crave constancy, but of a dynamic, not a static sort—new experience can serve to reconfirm as well as threaten. "Journeys end in lovers meeting"; but the fewer the journeys, the fewer the meetings—and much delight is lost.

In good marriages there is a little leeway, as it were—a striving toward an ideal, but not compulsively. Mature people, then, do not demand or even desire a flat continuity, but see a certain amount of playful interest in others besides the husband or wife as a norm, and use it to advantage not only individually but mutually. If, however, duplicity comes into the picture, the relationship is seriously threatened.

Again, though, what of the *troublesome* infidelities? Here we have to assess the symptom (the unfaithful attitudes or behaviour), to determine what it indicates about the causes and gravity of the underlying stresses, and also assess it in regard to the effects it produces. If the symptom connotes continuous dissatisfactions, do these exist because of disorder in the unfaithful spouse—immaturity, character disorder, neurosis, and so on, and to what degree—or is the problem preponderantly the partner's; or if, as usual, both are contributing, how, how much, and why? Are the effects such as to put the relationship in real jeopardy, and if so, why or why not? Are these people perhaps oversensitive; or are they too bland and phlegmatic?

How much anxiety, guilt, and shame are involved for the unfaithful one? How much real risk is run of the complete loss of a relationship that still has potential value? Is there evidence of foolish indiscretion or blatant flouting of mores? Are children threatened in their security or in their potential for healthy development?

Even at the level of extramarital intercourse, such questions must be raised and answers sought with cool objectivity, not with the heat of indignation or the cold condemnation of contempt.

An additional area that may be pertinent concerns the relationship between the unfaithful partner and his (or her) other love. How much is fantasy, how much real object love? How responsible are these people and how capable of standing fast against threats to their individual and mutual best interests or the reasonable interests of others?

All these questions point to the need for vast care and wisdom in evaluating infidelity at any level. It must be seen in context, that is, against the individual and marital backgrounds and evaluated accordingly as behavior reflecting one way in which this person may be attempting to find gratification for deep-rooted desires and aspirations.

MORAL AND THEOLOGICAL CONSIDERATIONS

We have thus far made no allusion to moral or religious attitudes toward infidelity. In the section on evaluation, reference was made to the context of the infidelity in the individual and in the marriage; and this context must include the person's moral and religious views and standards and their depth and significance. On the other hand at no point should there be raised the question of the "rightness" or "wrongness" of behavior as measured against an authoritarian or religious standard of "good" or "bad." This is because the private beliefs of the therapist or counselor (we assume that he is reasonably healthy) should be expected not to influence him one way or another in making a diagnosis or carrying out a course of counseling or therapy. Least of all should he blame or condemn or despise, neither in the sense of branding attitudes or behavior as wicked nor in the sense of scorning them as foolishly constricted or prissy.

Physicians are consulted on medical matters; lawyers purvey legal advice; philosophers deal with moral questions; clergymen are the resource when problems of religion arise—and psychiatrists, caseworkers, psychologists, and counselors, who have their own work, do what *they do* (as professionals) and stay outside these other areas.

If it happens that a clergyman is interested in counseling, he must assume the burden of making sure that his personal concern with spiritual matters or beliefs does not offset or interfere with his ability to be compassionate but objective as a counselor; and when *any* caseworker or therapist suspects personal bias in himself (for any reason) to be impinging on his work, he should correct the situation immediately, seek consultation or treatment, or refer the case elsewhere.

PREVENTION

In cases in which infidelity is symptomatic of disorder and troublesome, it would be well to try to prevent the underlying stresses from arising. The best way for ensuring good marriages is to rear children well so that they have the best opportunity to turn out to be reasonably adult and healthy and likely to be able to assume their roles in marriage fairly easily. If this is done, and barring very difficult situational reactions, they can go about working out their problems with self-confidence and success. The working out of the problems—which always arise—is the key. It requires from the start an orientation toward the ideal of fidelity—not a compulsive orientation but a steady one. This requires that each partner assume that he will be a sort of anchor for the other, that he will be trustworthy in the short run and the long, and that he will try continually to understand the person he has married.

Although words are by no means enough to carry the whole relationship (Eliza Doolittle says "Show me!"), talk is immensely important: all sorts of talk, about feelings, ideas, impulses, fears, aspirations; talk in gratitude and praise; talk in remonstrance and criticism; talk in success and failure, in tenderness and anger; talk in inquiry, explanation, and apology; and mainly talk in sincerity. The quality counts far more than the quantity; and this kind of conversation demands hard thinking before the words come out, and patience and forbearance in the hearing of them. The hard thinking will tend to cut down on the need to say some things, at least.

Time is another requisite, not only for the talking and the doing of things together but for individual privacy; and time, in another sense, must be allowed for things to settle a bit, or for a new understanding to be integrated.

Consultation and support are not to be despised. In other times they came more easily, since family groupings were closer and experienced, friendly people near at hand. Lacking this kind of resource, if talk and time still leave issues unresolved, tried friends and physicians and clergymen *who are known to be mature, objective, and kindly* can help tremendously in offering support and clarification.

Generally speaking it is better, in the face of stress or of uncertain motivations, to avoid action that might aggravate the trouble, and married people are usually well advised not to act on impulses toward infidelity until the ramifications and effects of such action are clearly understood. The ability to renounce is an essential part of healthy human equipment.

When the best efforts of the partners fail and the best that friends, the family physician, or the clergyman may be able to do still leave too much of stress, then surely it is time for strictly professional help—and *before* the stresses become too great. How much professional help will be required from psychiatrist, social worker, marriage counselor, clinical psychologist, or other qualified professional will depend on the nature and severity of the difficulties that each partner brings to the relationship and marriage. The choice of therapist, too, will depend upon the nature of the problem; and if properly qualified, the person consulted will either take the case or refer it, according to whether his skills equip him to deal competently with the problem or make referral wiser.

TREATMENT

Obviously, infidelity has no specific or specialized treatment. Like any other behavior, it is referable to a personality, and since it occurs only within the framework of a marriage relationship, referable to that personality in relation to at least one other personality, and usually to two or more. The personalities must be understood and the relationships must be understood; treatment, as may be indicated, will follow.

Chapter 9

Divorce: Some Selected Repercussions

JAMES H. S. BOSSARD, A.M., Ph.D., L.H.D.

I

DIVORCE is a peculiarly American problem. More divorces are granted in the United States each year than in the rest of the world combined.[1] Selecting the year 1951, when comparable data with most other countries are available, the United States reported 381,000 divorces. Accepting this number as accurate for the time being, it exceeds by 235,000 the total number granted in Canada, England, Wales, France, West Germany, Yugoslavia, Sweden, Switzerland, and Japan. The United States, with a population three-fifths as large as the combined total for the countries just named, had granted one and three-fifths times as many divorces as they did. Making the comparison on the basis of the number of divorces for that year per 1,000 married couples, the rate in the United States is 10.4, as compared with 1.7 for Canada, 4.9 for Sweden, 2.8 for England and Wales, 5.3 for West Germany, and 6.5 for Yugoslavia and Japan.

The number of divorces given for the United States are official estimates, made on the basis of those states making annual reports. These reports admittedly are incomplete, nor do they include those divorces of Americans granted in other coun-

[1] United Nations, *Demographic Yearbook, 1954,* Statistical Office of the United Nations, New York, 1954, pp. 614–22.

97

tries. The actual number, therefore, may be assumed to be larger; how much larger, is uncertain.

It is equally clear that such data must be considered cumulatively. That is to say, each year's total must be added to those of the preceding years if one is interested in the total number of persons involved. Thus in the eight-year period 1946–1953 inclusive, a total of 3,442,000 divorces were reported as granted in the United States. Multiplied by two, this means that about seven million matrimonial mates passed through the experience of divorce during the eight-year period.

Obviously, then, no book about American family life can avoid the subject of divorce, and no book on psychiatry can overlook its impact upon the personalities and mental hygiene of those involved. Accordingly, the remainder of this chapter will present (1) some empirical studies of various aspects of the problem and (2) some selected effects upon the persons who are divorced.

II

SELECTED STUDIES OF DIVORCED PERSONS

1. In 1930 the late Willard Waller published a study of the aftereffects of divorce, based on thirty-three case histories of divorced persons.[2] Attention was focused upon the sociopsychological problems that followed divorce. The central core of his conclusions was that the breaking up of a family and the reconstruction of the personalities involved are complicated processes. He emphasized the importance of the social attitudes toward divorce in general and toward the divorced person in particular, that the effects of the experience involve the person's feelings, efficiency, and conception of the self, that there are often strong

[2] Willard W. Waller, *The Old Love and the New: Divorce and Readjustment*, published originally as a doctoral thesis at the University of Pennsylvania, and subsequently published by Liveright Publishing Corporation, New York, 1930, under the title *The Old Love and the New*.

temptations toward vagaries of conduct during the transition period, and that the reorganization of living patterns after the divorce involves the affectional, sexual, social, and occupational aspects of life. There is a certain timelessness about the insights presented by this study which gives it a value as unique now as when it was written.

2. An ecological study of the residential distribution of divorced women in Philadelphia, made by the author of this chapter in collaboration with Thelma Dillon, reveals some significant facts. The study was based on United States census data for 1930, and the spatial distribution of the 5,644 divorced women enumerated in 1930 was analyzed by the 404 census tracts utilized in the census of that year. The main conclusions are presented in summary in the following words:

. . . two facts concerning the spatial distribution of divorced women stand out clearly. First, they seek out areas of dense population, characterized by activity, mobility, and anonymity, and where housing conditions make possible a certain independence of residence. On the other hand, they avoid areas of sparse population, of spatial isolation, and of religious prejudice. The divorced woman presents, then, essentially a study in social isolation. She seeks the distractions of city life, but selects areas where she may be socially isolated. She seeks escape in the crowd, not in the wilderness. She wants human contacts, but avoids prying eyes. She places a premium upon privacy, and finds it in a crowded apartment house. She seeks friends, not in the continued associations of a primary group, but in come-and-go relations with a mobile neighborhood. It is this characterizing search—for stimulation, coupled with secrecy, for contact, with relatively less communication—which seems to offer the basic key to the spatial distribution of divorced women in Philadelphia.[3]

3. A lengthening series of studies deals with the subject of remarriage, with particular reference to the remarrying tend-

[3] James H. S. Bossard and Thelma Dillon, "The Spatial Distribution of Divorced Women—A Philadelphia Study," *American Journal of Sociology*, vol. 40, p. 507, January, 1935.

encies of divorced persons. These show (1) that almost one-fifth (18 per cent) of all marriages are remarriages, (2) that the divorced tend to remarry in greater proportion than do the widowed, chiefly perhaps because of the age differences between the two groups, (3) that three-fourths of all ever-divorced persons remarry within five years after their divorce, as compared with only one-half of widowers and one-fourth of widows, (4) that while those who remarry are more likely to select a partner from those who have been married than would occur by chance alone, divorced men tend to marry divorced women, rather than widows, and (5) that divorced women tend to mate with divorced men to an even greater extent.[4]

4. The question of the stability of remarriages of divorced persons and their happiness in subsequent marriages has received considerable attention in recent years. The investigations made in this area show a variety of approaches to the problem and differences in conclusions, often somewhat contradictory. There are, for example, the earlier findings of Paul Popenoe, based on his clinical experience, that the happiness ratings of the divorced who remarry are approximately the same as those of the never divorced.[5] One study of his, on the remarriage of divorced persons to each other, shows that, of 200 cases, 96 (48 per cent) were happy on the second attempt, 29 (15 per cent) were doubtful, and 75 (37 per cent) were definitely unhappy.[6]

Another approach has utilized marital-adjustment tests and

[4] James H. S. Bossard, *Marriage and the Child,* University of Pennsylvania Press, Philadelphia, 1940, pp. 129–34; Paul C. Glick, "First Marriages and Remarriages," *American Sociological Review,* vol. 14, pp. 728–32, December, 1949; Charles E. Bowerman, "Assortative Mating by Previous Marital Status: Seattle, 1939–1946," *American Sociological Review,* vol. 18, pp. 170–77, April, 1953; James H. S. Bossard, "Marrying Late in Life," *Social Forces,* vol. 29, pp. 404–408, May, 1951; Jessie Bernard, *Remarriage,* The Dryden Press, Inc., 1956, pt. III.

[5] Paul Popenoe, *Modern Marriage,* The Macmillan Company, New York, 1940, pp. 118–19.

[6] Paul Popenoe, "Remarriage of Divorcees to Each Other," *American Sociological Review,* vol. 3, p. 696, October, 1938.

scores. Terman's study can be cited as an example here. This shows very slight difference between the remarriages of divorced persons and those married but once.[7] Finally, there are the studies of Locke and Klausner, based on California and Indiana studies, which conclude that the divorced woman who remarries is as good a risk in the second marriage as not previously married women are in their first marriages. Divorced men, on the other hand, have somewhat lower chances of happiness in marriage than men in first marriages.[8]

5. A return to concern with the problems of adjustment of divorced persons is found in a recent volume by Goode, in which he presents and analyzes data from 425 women in the Detroit area who had been divorced. Ten of the twenty-two chapters of this detailed study deal with after-the-divorce problems. Among the many findings are the following:

1. The time of greatest disturbance is the time of final separation.

2. The other people about whom divorced women are concerned are not the general public, but the social groups of which they are members.

3. The trauma attending and following divorce is greatly influenced by the active approval or disapproval of these social groups.

4. Divorced women are handicapped by the lack of clearly defined patterns of adjustment expected of them.

5. Remaining ties with the former mate, emotions of love or

[7] Lewis M. Terman, *Psychological Factors in Marital Happiness*, McGraw-Hill Book Company, Inc., New York, 1938, p. 418. See also Lewis M. Terman and Paul Wallin, "The Validity of Marriage Prediction and Marital Adjustment Tests," *American Sociological Review*, vol. 14, pp. 497–504, August, 1949.

[8] Harvey J. Locke, *Predicting Adjustment in Marriage: A Comparison of a Divorced and a Happily Married Group*, Henry Holt and Company, Inc., New York, 1951, chap. 14; Harvey J. Locke and William Klausner, "Prediction of Marital Adjustment of Divorced Persons in Subsequent Marriages," *Proceedings of the Pacific Society, Research Studies of the State College of Washington*, vol. 16, pp. 30–33, 1948.

hate, sense of guilt, and lingering feelings of responsibility appear, singly or in combination, as one moves from case to case.[9]

III

The third section of this chapter is devoted to certain highlights in the experiences of divorce and its aftermath. The discussion is based upon the author's collection of twenty-four case histories. Twenty of these concern men who were divorced and four are about women. Contact with one of these cases covered thirty-six years; two, thirty-two years; three, thirty years; and the others, periods of varying length, but all less than thirty years. None of these cases was explored in terms of an organized, systematic enquiry, but in all but two cases, contact was close and repeated during crisis periods. This section will record, then, selected impressions crystallized by these cases.

1. The social attitude toward divorce is of basic importance. The significance of any form of conduct depends upon the evaluation that society attaches to it. Society is constantly defining and appraising behavior. The mores, the late William Graham Sumner reminded us years ago, can make anything right or wrong. Divorce, as one form of very conspicuous behavior, comes in for a full measure of such evaluation.

The social attitude that is especially important is particular, not general. What matters to the divorced person is not so much what the general public thinks but, as Goode has pointed out, what the social groups of which he or she is a member will think or say. Concretely speaking, this means family members and other kinsfolk, friends, leisure-time companions, work associates, church contacts, and the like. These are the people who matter. It is the hesitance about their attitudes that explains the search for social isolation, revealed in the study of the resi-

[9] William J. Goode, *After Divorce*, The Free Press, Glencoe, Illinois, 1956. The reader is also referred to the more generalized study of remarriage and its problems by Jessie Bernard, *op. cit.*

dential distribution of divorced women previously mentioned.

Concerning these group attitudes, it is important to emphasize that they have two dimensions. One is spatial, meaning that these attitudes vary from place to place. Such variations may be regional, changing from North to South to Midwest to Far West; or grow out of the dominant religion of the people of an area —Jewish, Mennonite, Catholic, or Baptist; or reveal the national origin of the population. Usually these basic factors combine to accentuate the differences, so that the French Canadian Catholic community in New England is markedly different in attitude from an Irish Catholic district in south Philadelphia, or from an old-family area in the Deep South. Differences in the ways that behavior is defined are not confined, of course, to divorce but include every item in the code. Nor is there necessarily any consistency in the pattern of behavior that is approved. One knows, for example, a community where several young women are in varying stages of pregnancy, or have given birth to children, before their marriage, without seeming loss of status, yet divorce in this area is a lasting disgrace. Possibly the reader can identify, without too much effort, communities where the reverse combination prevails.

The other dimension is that of time. Social attitudes change from time to time. Speaking generally, the public attitude toward divorce has changed completely since World War I. The former prime minister of Great Britain was divorced; so was the presidential candidate on the Democratic ticket in 1956. In an earlier decade, many Americans, in their devotion to the late Franklin Roosevelt, developed a new tolerance because of the divorces in his immediate family.

2. These attitudes toward divorce express themselves often in an oblique way. A French philosopher once expressed the essence of this when he said: "There is something in the misfortunes of our best friends which does not altogether displease us." It is not cynical but only realistic to point out that when,

for example, a man fails in business, or his children turn out badly, or his wife leaves him, one can detect, if one is alert, that behind the expressions of sympathy there lurks a certain undercurrent of satisfaction because this misfortune has happened to someone else and not to oneself. At times there may even be a touch of malice. "Oh, that poor woman," says Mrs. Brown. "I feel so sorry for her. And she was such a good wife." What Mrs. Brown really means is: "That ought to reduce Betty Smith to her proper size. She won't be going around with her nose up in the air for a while at least."

3. There is another characteristic about people that bears upon the significance of social attitudes. It is perhaps a vagary of human cruelty that we depreciate, subtly to be sure, people who have personal and emotional problems. Perhaps there is no way in which we are more cruel to each other than in this respect. A man (or woman) may swear like a trooper, lie habitually, steal, commit adultery, do all sorts of things, but if he seems well adjusted and agreeable we grope for extenuating circumstances. On the other hand one may be clean living and high minded, but if there are evidences of personal, and particularly *emotional*, problems, how very unfortunate!

What makes all this so strange is that all persons are emotional, at least in areas that touch them closely. In fact most of the recent gains in insight into human behavior suggest that emotions often play a larger role, and may be a better guide, in life than intelligence. At any rate there is the old saying that what separates man from the other animals is that he drinks without being thirsty and makes love at all seasons of the year. The basis of both of these activities would seem to be emotional.

4. Continuing in a realistic vein, the divorced person is not free from the envy of other unhappily married persons, who have not made any progress in working out their own problems. In fourteen of the case histories upon which these observations are based, the problems of the divorced persons were signally

complicated by factors that arose from such sources of envy. It seems as though people who are unhappily married often have a special animosity toward persons who work out their problem by being divorced and then starting over again. Jealousy is a strange and often vicious thing. Women, particularly, often envy divorced women, as well as appear unduly critical of widows. All the world loves a lover, it is said, but all the world does not love either a divorced or a widowed person.

The foregoing factors, presented with frankness here, need to be emphasized in any appraisal of the repercussions of divorce because they constitute the social and emotional milieu in which persons who have been divorced have to work out their problems.

5. The problems that divorced persons face vary with the circumstances of each particular case. In like manner, each person involved in the termination of a marriage is a separate individual, who will respond in his or her own way to a given situation. It renders a disservice to our understanding of this whole area of human experience to rush to hasty conclusions about what divorced persons as a group do or do not do, especially since these prognostications are based on a limited number of cases, and not always representative in kind. The comments that follow are intended, then, to be descriptive and general, with the particular purpose of throwing light on the variety of problems and responses apt to be encountered.

6. There are few, if any, cases where divorce does not carry with it painful or tragic experiences. This does not overlook the fact that divorce is often the solution to an intolerable situation, that many marriages are so unhappy that the actual steps of separation and divorce bring only liberation and relief, and that the persons involved show immediate improvement in health and general effectiveness. There are such cases, and there is no denial of them in anything that follows in this chapter.

7. In all cases, however, the steps involved in a divorce call for changes in the patterns of living that are open to public

notice. One or both partners leave their home, they locate elsewhere, their addresses are changed, so are their telephone numbers, and many other formal evidences. These are signals which are interpreted as failure or mistake in a very important area of life. And failures and mistakes are never pleasant to admit—publicly. Most of us have our failures, we make many mistakes, but they are trivial or limited in scope or known to but few persons. Failure in marriage is public. Everyone who knows you will find out about it. The better people know you, and the better known you are, the more they will be interested and eager to know all the details. These experiences are not pleasant, even for the outwardly callous and the inwardly serene.

What failure means to people and does to them is something about which too little is known. One sees curious and devious evidence of the seriousness with which it is regarded. In dealing with college students who are dropped for scholastic failures or behavior delinquencies, it is significant how frequently parents, kinsfolk, as well as the students themselves, plead for some arrangement that will save face and permit the erring one to return to his or her community in such a way and at such a time as will avoid public knowledge of the failure involved. If this is true in matters of this kind, how much more serious is the public acknowledgment of failure in marriage.

8. At times the sense of failure may be mingled with feelings of guilt. These are the persons who, while going through the divorce proceedings and afterward, will keep thinking: "Perhaps if I had tried a little longer," or "If only I had done so and so," or "If only I had been more patient." The human mind is a cunning thing, often berating us for doing what it has already told us is the only thing that could be done. There are, to be sure, those who berate themselves, vaguely or quite consciously, for just the reverse. For years they had not done the inevitable. They themselves had not been happy, their mates had not been happy, only pride or inertia or shame or fear had kept them

from taking the step. Now that it is being taken, there is a sense of guilt, not for what is being done but for that which was not done years before.

9. Separation and divorce mean not only the termination of old ways of living, old associations, and old habits, but the development of new ones. The reorganization of living habits is an inevitable aftermath of divorce. Married life is, from one standpoint, a series of habits. Some of these habits grow out of the division of labor—the wife does certain things, the husband does others. In a study of family rituals made by Dr. Eleanor Stoker Boll and the author, it was shown how much of family living comes to be a routine process, part of which hardens into rituals.[10] Now when a marriage is terminated, these old habits must be discarded and new ones formed amid new surroundings. This is far easier said than done, for family habits are very detailed and pervasive and the readjustment of so many of these at one time is often a difficult process. Perhaps the reader has had the experience of moving from one house to another. If so, it may be easy to recall the manifold task of readjusting even the most prosaic of living habits. And many of the habits of family living together are far from prosaic, even in less happy homes.

10. The readjustment of the affectional and sexual life of the divorced is not a simple process. The expressions of these are partly habitual, perhaps more so than many persons are willing to concede. But they are more than habits. They represent needs to which the divorced have become accustomed, in some way and to some extent at least, and new satisfactions come to be sought sooner or later. These may take a variety of forms. In some cases the new freedom finds expression in a degree of promiscuity, as though for purposes of experimentation. In other cases, the readjustment takes the form of a selective bohemianism, temporary, too, perhaps. Then there are the cases where the divorced

[10] James H. S. Bossard and Eleanor Stoker Boll, *Ritual in Family Living*, University of Pennsylvania Press, Philadelphia, 1950.

pair continue to have sex relations with each other, perhaps for extended periods of time and after both have remarried with other persons. In still other instances, there is the healing sublimation found in creative work or religious zeal. Or perhaps there is a quick, almost compulsive attachment to another person—the well-known rebound cases. Finally, and fortunately, in most cases there is the promising comfort of a new marriage.

11. Social relations often present a problem after divorce. Married couples do not live in a social vacuum. They have their friends, varying in number and closeness of relationship. Some may be carry-overs of premarital days; others may have been acquired after marriage. Now that the married pair have separated, who will socialize with whom? Who will invite the husband? The wife? What would happen if both appeared at the same function? Friends may hesitate to see either one; it would be like taking sides in the marital split. One or both tend to be left alone, yet this may be the very time when friendly contacts mean most.

Of course the problem of social contacts varies a great deal, depending on circumstances. In a large city, people tend to have contacts with many specialized groups. Many of these contacts are limited or impersonal, with little reference to one's personal life. In a small town the situation is quite different. Or the predivorce activities of the couple may be important. When the superintendent of the Sunday school is being divorced from the head of its primary department in a church in a small inland town, the complications are highly charged with community drama.

To meet the problems of social relationships, varying patterns of adjustment appear. Some divorced persons withdraw from all social contacts and become recluses—for the time being at least. Or one of the couple withdraws and leaves the social field to the other. Many of the arrangements for the postdivorce period are arrived at by the couple before their separation, and division of social contacts may be one of these. In still other cases, old friends are avoided and a whole new circle is developed. But such readjustments are not easy, nor can one make a turnover of satisfactory friendships in a week. Much depends here upon the age and inner resiliency of the persons involved. Also, the problem for the divorced man and for the divorced woman tends to differ in many respects.

12. The meaning of divorce for the occupational career of those divorced cannot be too strongly emphasized. If the divorced woman has been a housewife, she may be faced with the task of earning a living. For women who had occupational experience before marriage, there is only the task of their reestablishment in the workaday world. For older women, without previous job experience, or for those who have been away from out-of-the-home employment for some years, the difficulties are more pronounced. Older women as such have less appeal in the labor market.

But men may have their difficulties, too. It is here that the subtleties of human envy and malice come into play, particularly for men who are employed at the higher occupational levels—in the professions, the administrative posts, in positions of prominence and responsibility. "Oh, yes, John is a very able person. Under normal circumstances he would be just the man. But you know he is divorced. There was some talk, you know. I don't know how people would take it. Better play it safe." Thus speaks John's envious associate, in spite of the fact that John has never been so happy and efficient as he has been since his divorce. "Oh, Harry would never do as a candidate for mayor. His divorce, you know. The Catholic vote would be solid against him." This from the second-rate aspirant, his own moral record not above reproach.

13. No mention has been made of the problems that grow out of the presence of children in divorce cases. These are being considered in another chapter. Suffice it to say here that each

of the preceding situations is complicated, and the problems resulting are accentuated by the presence of children. Children add another dimension to the aftermath of divorce.

14. Finally, this chapter would not be complete without reference to the character of the persons involved. In many ways this is the basic factor that determines how the postdivorce problems will be dealt with. And the greatest differences prevail here. Some people who go through the travail of divorce bounce right back, buoyant with hope for another trial at marital happiness; some have the capacity to view their problems objectively, face them honestly, and deal with them resolutely. There are those who have the ability to learn from experience and, chastened by a first failure, are the better prepared for another marriage.

But there are those whose responses are less fortunate. Among these are the persons who become embittered by what they have gone through. In addition to their marital experiences, they may have had unscrupulous attorneys to deal with (several of our cases report this, women particularly); the masters appointed to conduct the hearings may have been crudely unsuited to the testifying applicant (would that judges assumed more responsibility for appointing masters on a par with the persons whose complaints they will hear); they may have been embittered because the other mate sought to blacken their name or failed to abide by preseparation contracts. Whatever the percentage of such cases in the entire ensemble, to the particular victims they constitute 100 per cent of the cases.

Responses of another kind are where the agonies of spirit find expression in physical and mental illness. Here is an important field of psychosomatic medicine. Or there are the persons who develop defensive patterns, designed to operate below the level of consciousness to protect from hurt or restore an equilibrium that has been upset. Then, too, there are the internal conflicts and tensions that result when the legal severance of the marriage has not been accompanied by a severance of the emotional bond. If the break with the past is not complete, there cannot but appear the residues of remorse or indecision or uncertainty. When the tie that once was lingers on, it may burn an uncertain fuse.

15. It would be naïve to overlook the conflicts that arise for some of the divorced because of moral or religious qualms. The century-old preachment of marriage as a holy estate, the universal expectation of its permanence, the accumulated traditions of the family group, all of these tend to raise an issue of doubt for some divorced people on the propriety of what they have done, whatever the merits of the case may have been. True, the courts dissolve, but what God has joined together, let no man put asunder.

Chapter 10

Divorce Problems as Seen by the Clinician

MARTIN GOLDBERG, M.D.

EVERYONE is aware that divorce and separation are commonplace occurrences in our culture today. It follows, therefore, that many people will bring personal and family problems centering around divorce to the clinician. (The term "clinician" is used in this chapter to denote all the various trained experts to whom people turn for help, including physicians, clinical psychologists, social caseworkers, pastoral counselors, and so on.)

In his lucid chapter on the sociological repercussions of divorce, Dr. Bossard stresses the fact that the greatest upset and disturbance in the spouses occur at the time of final separation. He also emphasizes their fear of the disapproval of the immediate social group (friends, family, and so on). The clinician sees these sociological phenomena in terms of an *individual*—or of two individuals—who is confused, apprehensive, and badly in need of help. Generally, a large part of the help that the person seeks consists of finding someone who will listen with genuine objectivity to his problems. In virtually every case, the troubled spouse has first sought such help from members of the family or close friends. But the inherent personal problems and biases of relatives and friends in most instances mitigate against the ability to be of assistance. Confused by the opinions and advice thrust on him, apprehensive that he will incur social disapproval, troubled by the imminence of a major change in his way of living, the spouse with a divorce problem may finally seek out the trained clinical expert. What the clinician then encounters is a person who knows he is in trouble and needs help but rarely realizes the actual nature of his difficulties.

Effective counseling in divorce problems follows the same principles of counseling in any situation. Various clinicians, depending on their training and theoretical orientation, will tend to emphasize different aspects of the helping process. Thus one counselor may use a so-called intuitive approach which emphasizes the relationship aspects of counseling. Another may concentrate on the development of understanding and insight, utilizing interpretations and "working them through." The success or failure of the helping process is apt to depend far more on the sincerity, maturity, and interest of the counselor, and his respect for the client as an individual with potentials for growth, than on any marked variations in technique and approach. Experience has shown, however, that there are certain major points of consideration for the clinician in a divorce problem. Among these, the following may be mentioned:

1. In divorce situations the giving of advice is not only a poor technique which can serve only to confuse the client further, but it may also be an infringement on the areas of operation and competency of the legal profession. The effective counselor eschews all forms of advice-giving, with the realization that such techniques cannot help his client to work out his own problems. At the same time the counselor does not confuse the giving of advice with the giving of information. The latter is a perfectly legitimate and useful function of the helping process and might be exemplified by the imparting of knowledge pertaining to sexual adjustment, as described in Chapter 2.

2. A major portion of the counselor's work consists in helping the individual (or couple) to recognize his real needs and dif-

ficulties and then formulate his own realistic goals. On the one hand he must be careful not to accept at face value the client's statements of his apparent needs and goals, since these are frequently confused or neurotically distorted. On the other hand it is even more damaging and erroneous for the counselor to introduce into the helping process any version of his own needs or aims. In divorce situations, this is apt to occur when the counselor is strongly motivated to "save" marriages or hold families together. Counselors with rigidly held, dogmatic theoretical views concerning psychodynamics and human interaction may also fall into the trap of substituting their own goals for the client's. This is frequently seen as an insistence on "full understanding" or "insight," when such is not the concern of the person in difficulty. People have recovered from severe emotional illness with little or no insight into what was wrong with them.

3. Under the general category of "divorce problems," the clinician will encounter a tremendously wide spectrum of intrapsychic, interpersonal, and sociocultural difficulties. Psychoneuroses, alcoholism, sexual perversions, psychoses, situational maladjustments, and a host of other conditions may figure prominently in the individual case. Therefore, the well-established principle of considering each "divorce problem" as a distinctive, unique situation that must be thoroughly explored for understanding is a *sine qua non* of effective counseling.

The following three situations, all of which were encountered in clinical practice (by a psychiatrist in this instance), serve to point out the greatly varying needs of people who present themselves as "wanting a divorce." They also indicate the need for a flexible approach on the clinician's part, one fitted to the client rather than to any dogmatic theoretical conceptions.

Mrs. A was a thirty-year old housewife who came to the physician and described great unhappiness in her life. She attributed all her problems to her marriage and her husband. She felt that he did not pay enough attention to her and was ignoring their four children. In short he was ruining her life. The answer to all her difficulties seemed to her to be a divorce. She asked that the physician see her husband also and "help" her to get a separation or divorce. Except to see herself as the innocent victim, Mrs. A did not feel that she was in any way connected with all the unhappiness around her.

In evaluating Mrs. A initially, the physician-counselor elicited from her a detailed summary of her early family life and background. Both her parents were professional people; her father was a busy, successful man, preoccupied with his work, and her mother was an equally busy and successful woman who had never given up her career, except for the brief interlude of time necessary to bear her one child. During the patient's entire childhood, including the earliest years, she was in the care of various hired governesses and housekeepers, who seemed cruel, restrictive, and unloving to her. She saw very little of her parents and felt that they had no interest in her. Miserably unhappy throughout her childhood, she blamed all her anguish on her parents.

As Mrs. A described this background it became clear that her unhappiness was not something stemming only from her husband and marriage but had been a part of her since her earliest remembered years. With specific questioning, she modified her original statements to indicate that probably her husband actually did pay her and the children a good deal of attention, though still not enough to satisfy her. She responded quickly to the physician's statement that what she seemed to need was not "help in getting a divorce" but help in arriving at an understanding of the real causes of the misery and unhappiness inside her.

Without going into a detailed explanation of Mrs. A's psychodynamics and with a minimum of speculation, it can be seen that she carried over a feeling of being neglected and unwanted from her childhood experience with her parents and projected it onto her present situation and onto her husband. She also identified strongly with her children, constantly feeling any lack of attention paid to them by her husband as a hurtful rejection of herself.

In short Mrs. A was an individual with a long-standing personality disorder characterized by much distortion of her feelings. Her initial talk of wanting a divorce reflected her desire for a profound change. Although she did not consciously recognize that the change had to start in her, but rather projected this into a desire for a change in marital status, her action in coming to a psychiatrist (rather than a lawyer, for example) indicates some unconscious awareness of her real needs.

Mrs. B was a twenty-year-old married college student who had consulted the college Student Health Service asking for help with problems about her marriage. She was referred to the physician for evaluation and treatment. In her first interview with the physician-counselor she said, rather thoughtfully, that she believed she wanted a divorce. However, she was confused and hoped the physician could help her to see the situation and her feelings about it more clearly.

Mrs. B had been married at the age of seventeen to a young man who had lost both legs in action with the armed forces during World War II. Reviewing her personal history, she stated that she had been born and raised in a small midwestern farming community. Unattractive as a youngster, she had been somewhat unhappy in her social contacts throughout childhood and adolescence. She had conceived of herself as inferior and unable to fit in with people. Her home life was somewhat happier and more secure with her parents, who were a bit strict and old-fashioned but reasonably loving and accepting. At times, however, she felt overshadowed by her two older brothers who were more important in the family constellation because of their services on the family farm.

Mrs. B was aware that her background had been conducive to making her rather dependent on home and family and afraid of the outside world. In addition, she had a tendency to compensate for feelings of personal inadequacy in the social sphere by concentrating on intellectual pursuits and studies. After graduating from high school at an early age, she mustered up enough courage to leave home and enter college, where she soon met her husband-to-be who was a law student in the same university. Like many amputees, he had apparently made a good adjustment to his handicap and was an extremely popular and respected "big man on campus." When he became interested in our patient she was overwhelmed. Never before had anyone outside her home treated her with such attention and affection, and being the girl friend of the campus hero brought her much needed status and respect from other students. On a less conscious level, she was attracted by her husband-to-be's handicap, since it allowed her to be the dominant, aggressive partner of the match. This gave her some feelings of winning out in competition with men, which were important to her because of her early relationship with brothers and parents. Again, one could speculate about many other factors that attracted this couple to each other, but in any case, after a brief courtship they were married with the blessings of both families.

During subsequent interviews, Mrs. B told the therapist of the changes that took place during her three years of marriage. While participating in various activities of college life, she gained considerably in sophistication and social confidence. Soon she became aware that she was no longer an unattractive adolescent but a woman who was generally regarded by her increasing number of friends as handsome, intelligent, and poised. Her gains in security were considerable and her self-evaluation rose markedly. As her own personality matured, however, she began to find that her marriage was no longer meeting her rapidly changing needs. When first married, she had rather enjoyed the fact that her husband was, of necessity, dependent on her to perform many of the duties usually handled by the man in a marriage. But as the initial enthusiasm of finding someone who liked and was attentive to her wore off, and as she developed more confidence in herself as a woman, she found herself resenting more and more the necessity to be the dominant, aggressive partner in the marriage.

After seeing Mrs. B a number of times the physician held interviews with her husband on several occasions at the request of both spouses. Mr. B proved to be a very likable, intelligent young man who had originally been most intent on keeping the marriage intact. Now, however, he was becoming increasingly confused and dissatisfied with the changes in his wife. He was troubled with tendencies to be passive and nonassertive, some of which may have been basic in his character structure and some undoubtedly secondary to his physical handicap. In order to help him with his feelings and problems, the physician referred him to another psychiatrist for treatment, which he willingly accepted. He was sent to a different doctor because it was evident that husband and wife had widely differing goals in terms of their marriage problem and needed individual rather than joint help. However, the two psychiatrists in the situation remained in close communication with each other on the matter.

Meanwhile, as Mrs. B continued to discuss her problem, she was becoming increasingly aware that the marriage was failing to meet her needs. She clearly voiced her desire for a divorce but feared the censure she believed she would receive from all sides. Her strict, old-fashioned parents were very much against any break-up in the marriage. She realized, too, that all her friends and society in general would be unsympathetic to her for leaving a popular, pleasant, and obviously handicapped person.

In this situation, Mrs. B looked to the therapist not so much for advice as for permission to air her feelings unhindered and uncriticized. She wanted to ascertain their validity for herself and the marriage. In a relatively short time she was able to formulate and carry out plans for a divorce. Even though divorce had never been his desire, her husband was able not only to accept it but actively to encourage his wife in what was right for her. Fulfilling an idea he had frequently mentioned, he moved back to his home town where he reestablished his earlier family and friendship ties and continued to be self-supporting in an excellent professional position. Several years later the former wife wrote to the doctor telling of her increasing happiness and of her solid, stable, and compatible second marriage.

Mrs. B was a very different woman from Mrs. A. In large part she had worked through most of her problems of attaining maturity before counseling with a physician. (The timing in this case is stressed because of the tendency of many authorities in the field of psychotherapy to imply that psychological growth and enlightenment can occur only as a result of therapy. Actually, this omnipotent attitude stems from the fact that the clinician rarely sees the many people who work through problems of maturing without formal help.) Mrs. B's purpose in coming to a psychiatrist to talk about a divorce was a rather healthy one of wanting to find a place where she could look at her own feelings and needs, free from the usual biases and conventions of social custom and popular prejudice. By her own persistence she finally achieved her goal.

Mrs. C, like the two women previously described, came to the physician stating that she wanted to talk about a divorce. She was a forty-two-year-old society club woman continuing to pursue a successful career and married for twenty-two years to a prominent professional man. Throughout most of their marriage they had been reasonably happy, although there had been a fair number of personality clashes and differences.

When she saw the physician for the first time, Mrs. C described her situation as one in which both she and her husband felt that they had nothing in common anymore, nothing to hold their marriage together. They had more or less calmly agreed to separate and obtain a divorce. Both of them felt, however, that it would be well to talk over the situation with a trained person before breaking up.

After twenty-one years of a childless marriage, Mrs. C had undergone a hysterectomy, a year prior to consulting the physician, professing to be unconcerned about both the operation and her lack of offspring. She felt that she and her husband had very different personalities and interests and that their separate, divergent courses had led them to a point where they had little to talk about and no common emotional meeting ground. Both considered themselves too intelligent and sophisticated to argue openly or fight over matters, and consequently their progressive estrangement had been marked by a minimal communication between them.

Because Mr. C was also very interested in discussing the situation and had about the same goals as his wife, the physician also saw him regularly. Mr. C described their marriage in essentially the same manner as Mrs. C had, differing on no major points.

The psychiatrist worked with both spouses in individual and joint interviews. During the counseling, a great deal of feeling on the part of both husband and wife was evidenced about their childlessness and about Mrs. C's hysterectomy, both revealing considerable inner disappointment because of their failure to have children and also viewing the hysterectomy as a calamitous sign of their increasing age and diminished vitality. Talking about these factors openly and together, the couple found that their disappointment was not so keen and troublesome when voiced openly and shared with each other. They realized how little sharing and communication there had been between them in recent years because of certain resentments, many of which centered around their very different personalities (the husband inclined to be rigid, perfectionistic, and introverted and the wife more flexible, outgoing, and social). With mutual discussion they were better able to see that their differences could serve complementary rather than antagonistic ends. Thus in less than a dozen interviews Mr. and Mrs. C had dropped all thought of separation or divorce and were seeking and planning new mutual interests and ways to continue to enrich their marriage, including plans for building a new house, their first "real home," to replace the swank but impersonal apartment they had been living in.

In retrospect it seems that Mrs. C, in wanting to see a physician "about a divorce" really needed a chance to explore her feelings about her marriage, approaching middle age, her hysterectomy, and so on. The great need was to recognize and correct the emptiness she felt and the gravely distorted communications that had evolved between her and her husband. Mr. C also used the experience to bring out his feelings of disappointment at not having children and a "home," and to realize that these were related to his apprehensions about advancing middle age. Both husband and wife came to see that the increasing sense of loneliness that was troubling them could be helped by their drawing closer together rather than by separating.

Here we have, then, three different women all of whom came to the same physician ostensibly for the same reason—"to talk about divorce." Their basic needs could hardly have been more different: in one case the need to recognize serious intrapsychic personality disturbances and come to grips with them; in the second to see a way clear to dissolving a marriage that had become unhealthy and limiting; and in the final case to clear up certain interpersonal conflicts that were breaking up a marriage both spouses basically wanted to continue.

Problems similar to these three are by no means uncommon and may come to the attention of any clinician. Particularly difficult are those situations similar to that of Mrs. B. Here, a spouse is struggling with a decision that is socially unpopular but still represents health and growth for the individual; that is, getting out of a marriage based on predominantly unhealthy needs that have been outgrown or otherwise mastered. It should be said, however, at this point that the counselor or therapist must not encourage hedonistic actions and thinking or complete disregard for the other individuals in such a situation. What he must do is be able to *recognize* and put aside his own social, moral, and religious biases so that he can honestly and completely *listen* to the troubled individual and allow him to reach his own decision as to what constitutes a mature solution. If this is a basically healthy decision for him it often precipitates the other partner also into the new and, hopefully, more constructive and healthy solution.

Recognizing the diversity of problems that people can bring to him in the guise of divorce situations, the clinician must evaluate each case individually and carefully and with as little distortion from his own feelings and biases as is possible, in order to help clients find the solution to their problems that is valid for the real needs of themselves and of their marriage partners.

Chapter 11

Marriage Adjustments and the Law

NOCHEM S. WINNET

ARRIAGE counselors seek means to influence and modify the interactional forces that arise in the marriage relationship when they cause difficulty for husband and wife involved. They are concerned with the emotional ties that hold individuals and families together and with the emotional strains that only too frequently tear them apart. They should therefore have an understanding of the legal concepts that tie individuals and families together and the legal consequences that result when the ties are torn apart. This is not to say that marriage counselors should also be lawyers; only, that an understanding of the law of the family relationship has utility and relevance for them. And since lawyers are frequently called upon in family and marriage disputes, I am certain that a knowledge of the principles of marriage counseling would be of equal usefulness to them.

Marriage is a contract in which the state has an interest. Ordinary contracts concern only the parties who make them. They can by mutual agreement terminate them. A breach of an ordinary contract entitles the offended party to damages. The state, however, prescribes the terms and conditions under which a contract can be made; it prescribes the conditions under which it may be terminated.

Who may enter such contracts? Single persons or properly divorced persons. Persons who get "easy" divorces in Mexico or in one of the states catering to such divorces may find themselves in great difficulty upon remarriage. Most states do not allow marriage between lineal descendants within certain degrees. Most of the statutes also provide age limitation for the issuance of a license to marry. Generally speaking, a minor cannot enter a marriage contract unless he or she has the consent of the parents or guardian. The statutes also prescribe the step necessary before a marriage can be performed, such as the obtaining of a license, blood tests, and the proper person who may perform the ceremony.

Common-law marriages are informal marriages based on mutual assent where the statutory requirements have not been complied with in whole or in part. They are recognized in many states and the subject of much litigation there and elsewhere. A widower and his housekeeper produce a claimed common-law marriage upon his death almost as certainly as a will produces relations. The only uniform requirement for validity is contractual, an agreement to be husband and wife. Without the mutual agreement the relationship will be regarded as meretricious. Cohabitation and holding out to the world that they are husband and wife are theoretically but proofs of the status. In many states, however, one or both of these proofs are required.

What are the rights of the parties after marriage? At one time, and not so many years ago, the legal effect was the union of the partnership into one legal person, and that was the husband. He assumed all responsibilities for (her) his wife's antenuptial debts as well as for her future torts and frauds. Her independent contracting power was lost. She could neither sue nor be sued apart from him. I have often wondered whether the double standards of morality are the effect of this merging of the legal person. The Code of Hammurabi, 2250 b.c., provides: "If the finger has been pointed at the wife of a man because of another man, for her husband's sake she shall throw herself into the river." No similar law required the husband to drown himself in similar circumstances.

There has been a gradual emancipation of the wife, and modern legislation has removed almost entirely the legal incapacities of married women. Each maintains separate property upon marriage unless they join them. They have freedom of contract and freedom to sue. They have the right to acquire control, sell, or lease any property. The husband is no longer liable for the antenuptial debts of the wife. The wife's separate property is not liable for the debts of the husband. She can retain her separate earnings and enter into any business, even become a partner in a business with her husband. As one case puts it: "Their disability is now exceptional and their capacity general."

In Pennsylvania, and probably in most states, about the only disability of coverture is the need of the spouse joining in a conveyance of real estate. A wife has a right of dower in her husband's real estate, and the husband has the right of courtesy in his wife's real estate. Joint property that is in both names, whether real or personal, is known as property by entireties. It is the property of both and the property of neither, and may become the property of either by survivorship. It cannot be made subject to the payment of the debts of one of the parties.

The husband must support the wife by providing her with necessaries, such as, food, clothing, shelter, and medical attendance, according to their station in life. The wife may purchase necessities and the husband becomes liable for the payment.

What are necessaries may be a difficult question to answer. Shelter, food, and medical attention are clearly necessaries. Is a fur coat or an automobile a necessity? This, of course, is dependent upon the earnings of the husband and his station in life. The husband, of course, is entitled to the obedience and services of his wife. If these obligations are to be measured by the husband's ability legally to enforce them, they are at the present time infinitesimal. Attempt at any physical coercion of the wife on the part of the husband will likely land him in jail.

The husband must provide the home. His choice of home is controlling if exercised in good faith. A wife must follow her husband to the place he selects.

Husbands and wives may not sue each other except for divorce or support or to recover their separate properties. They cannot sue each other for injuries, misconduct, or destruction of property, excluding, of course, criminal action or divorce. A deserted wife, however, may sue her husband on any cause of action.

A husband and wife may not testify against each other as to conversations occurring between them during the existence of their marriage relationship even after they have been divorced. They may testify in favor of each other. They may testify against each other in criminal proceedings for injury done to each other or to their minor children. They may sue each other and testify to recover their separate property or to answer when one attacks the character of the other.

Children are entitled to the protection and support of their parents. They are entitled to be supported according to the station in life of their parents who may be even criminally liable upon failure to protect and support. Correspondingly the parents are entitled to the custody, obedience, and services of their children. They are entitled to the earnings of a child during minority. On the other hand parents are not entitled to the unusual earnings of a child, such as the earnings of a gifted artist or actor. These earnings become a separate property of the child who is entitled to them just as he is entitled to any property that comes to him by reason of inheritance. The parents are not liable for the torts and wrongdoings of their children nor for their contracts except for such necessities that the child may have been required to purchase.

The separate property of the child, however, may be charged with the obligation to support parents if such parents have become or are likely to become a public charge. Parents may even be obliged to support an adult child if he be indigent.

Notwithstanding the disabilities of minors to contract other than necessities, they often do. The law gives a minor child the right to disaffirm any contract upon reaching maturity. These days when it is difficult to gauge the age of a child by appearance, a merchant must be on guard. The shock of an automobile dealer can well be imagined when he learns that the young man who purchased an automobile has disaffirmed his contract because he was not of age.

What are the rights of the parties upon termination of the family relationship? This can occur by separation of married parties, by divorce, or by death.

Considering death first, since it probably will be of least importance in the work of marriage counselors, the surviving spouse has an interest in the property, real and personal, the decedent has left. Under common law there are rights of dower and courtesy in each other's property. Each has a right to take one-third of the other's property. Each has a right to take one-third of the other's property no matter what the will of the decedent provides.

The laws of most states now specifically provide what shall be the rights of the survivor. Usually the surviving spouse is given a specific exemption of a sum of money. If the decedent left no issue and no kindred, then the entire estate goes to the survivor. If the decedent left a surviving spouse and no issue and some kindred, the wife is usually entitled to a specific sum of money (in Pennsylvania, ten thousand dollars) and one-half of the estate. If there survive a spouse and one child, the wife is entitled (in Pennsylvania) to one-half of the estate and the child the balance. If there are two or more children, the surviving spouse is entitled to one-third, the balance divided among the children.

The husband or wife may, of course, leave a will which determines how much the survivors shall receive. But there can be no disinheritance of each other unless there has been desertion. A surviving spouse may take action against the will and obtain such benefits as he or she would have received if the decedent died intestate, leaving no will.

Children, on the other hand, may be disinherited. A child born after the execution of a will takes as if the decedent died intestate.

Next in importance in the work of marriage counselors are the rights of the parties where the marriage is terminated by divorce.

The grounds for divorce are prescribed by statute and differ in each state. They may vary from none in number to thirteen. The usual are adultery, cruelty, drunkenness, drug addiction, desertion, abandonment, imprisonment for a felony, impotence, and indignities to the person. Where authorized by statute, cruelty is the common ground because courts have taken an extremely liberal view of the meaning of cruelty, and generally it is defined as such conduct as will make the continuance of marriage intolerable and unendurable from the standpoint of physical or mental health. The states that allow divorce for incompatibility are very few in number.

A divorce terminates the relationship of marriage. The decree of divorce may in some states provide for custody of the children. In most states no alimony is payable after the final decree is entered, since the relationship is at an end. There can, of course, be provision made for payment of the support of children.

A troublesome question frequently arises as to the obligation to support a wife after an "easy" divorce in a state other than the one in which the married couple resided. The United States Constitution required that every state give full faith and credit to the decrees of a sister state. At one time a husband could obtain a divorce in Nevada, or some other equally favorable state, and come back to his former place of residence and plead the decree as a bar to any further obligation to support his wife. As a practical matter this is no longer a good defense to an obligation of support. The United States Supreme Court has ruled that while one state must give full faith and credit to a decree of another state, nevertheless the court may inquire whether the jurisdiction for divorce was fraudulently obtained. Usually it is not too difficult to prove this, and if proven, the court will refuse to recognize the decree of the state granting the divorce and will impose an order of support.

Two other consequences of divorce may be briefly noted. If the parties own joint property they now become tenants in common, each owning one-half, and partition proceedings may be undertaken to divide either the property or the proceeds of the sale of the property. Annulment of a divorce is not frequently used. Generally speaking the same grounds entitling a party to a divorce entitle such party to an annulment.

Where there has been force or duress in constituting the marriage, annulment is frequently used. On the other hand courts have been unwilling to annul a marriage simply on the ground of the non-age of one of the parties. This is one instance where a minor cannot disaffirm a contract.

Marriage counselors are particularly and most frequently concerned with the rights and obligations of the parties when there is a separation without a divorce. The wife is, of course, entitled to be supported and loses it only on facts that would entitle the husband to a divorce. Children do not forfeit their right to support except at age. If the wife has means, and the husband is likely to become a public charge, she may have an obligation to support her husband.

Enforcing rights of support is one of the most serious problems confronting communities everywhere and particularly in metropolitan cities. Because of this and the social implications involved, almost every metropolitan city has a special division in its courts to handle domestic relations cases, where people may get aid from the court and its officers without the necessity of employing lawyers.

The procedure in Philadelphia might be illustrative of how the larger cities are attempting to handle the problem. Jurisdiction is in the Municipal Court of Philadelphia. It has a well-organized staff to handle these cases. Its intake department provides facilities for interviews and conferences, to give the parties an opportunity to discuss their grievances in the presence of a friendly court worker. These workers are not marriage counselors but probation officers who either by training or experience are qualified to make the initial attempt to resolve the differences between a husband and wife. In the initial stage, the opposite party is invited by letter to meet with the worker and the complainant to discuss the problem. If the respondent does not answer the invitation or if after the conference no agreement can be reached, the case proceeds to the second stage of the proceeding established in Philadelphia.

In this stage a social investigation is made of the parties and particularly the respondent. If necessary the parties are examined without cost by the court's medical staff. The respondent's employment record and earnings are determined, and the case is ready for the third stage which is the court hearing.

At the hearing the presiding judge has before him the report of the probation department and a résumé of the case. Because an effort for reconciliation has already been made, the judge himself does not ordinarily spend too much time attempting it. He will give the parties an opportunity to express their differences and troubles, and as most cases involve a claim for support, he will fix the amount of support or refuse the claim. Because of the thousands of cases that must be heard, this is about all the "adjustment" a court can make. Sometimes a reconciliation does take place in court. No study has ever been made to determine the effectiveness of such reconciliations.

The fourth and final stage of the court procedure is in the enforcement of the order. Respondents in support proceedings have a habit of falling in arrears on payments. Since a failure to pay in accordance with the order of the court is deemed a contempt, a respondent is summarily brought into court and given an opportunity to explain and justify his delinquency. Failure to do so results in a commitment to the county prison. The order of commitment provides that the respondent be released on paying in full or some substantial part of the arrearages. It is amazing how many of these respondents find the necessary moneys to pay into court rather than go to jail.

Are marriage adjustments really made by the legal process? Only if maintaining a status quo or continuing an armed truce in the family relationship can be so called. We do know some support orders run on for years. Some of the separated couples drift back together. Sometimes the courts have before them in support proceedings the children of couples who appeared years ago before them. No real evaluation has ever been made of the effectiveness of marital adjustments made in the courts.

On the other hand the courts and the legal process are doing an important and necessary job. Great progress has been made. The courts have since time immemorial been the place of refuge for the enforcement of marital obligations. Very early it was recognized that a civil remedy for a breach of the contract of support would be of no help to a wife or the children. By the time a suit was brought and answer filed, and the case came up for trial, the family might starve. Failure to support, therefore, was made a summary criminal offense and could be heard without a jury.

In every jurisdiction in the country, traditionally the failure to support is the basis of criminal proceedings. The defaulting spouse is arrested. This has all been changed in Pennsylvania without abandoning the criminal proceedings. There is now the alternative right of proceeding by petition against a defaulting spouse. This starts the process. No formal answer need be filed. No lawyer need be employed. A hearing is held as promptly as possible. The delay which now unfortunately occurs in a city like Philadelphia is due to the great number of cases that must be processed.

Deserting husbands who have fled the jurisdiction present a grave problem. Until a few years ago the only remedy of the deserted spouse was to bring expensive extradition proceedings and have the husband brought back to the state to answer the charge of desertion and nonsupport. Fortunately, many states have now adopted a Uniform Reciprocal Enforcement of Support Act which has as its purpose expediting extradition and obviating it by making the order imposed in one state enforceable in the state where the defendant is found. It provides that the person who submits to the order of the original state may be relieved from extradition. Upon the filing of a complaint showing a duty in the initial state, the court may not only enter an order to enforce the original order but can also punish for contempt upon failure to comply.

A frequent source of litigation between husband and wife after a separation is over custody of the children. The sole issue in such a case is the best interest of the child or children. The court may award custody to one and provide for visitation or sharing of custody by the other.

Generally speaking, the mother is favored in custody cases. Here, too, the facilities of the domestic relations court in a metropolitan city is used by the court in order to determine the best interest of the child. The medical staff and probation officers are available for investigation, study, and advice to the court.

Marriage counselors must recognize the role of the legal profession in marriage adjustments. Most persons who have marital difficulty think immediately of going "to see a lawyer." When a family dispute arises, whether it involves a separation, divorce, or custody, the usual first thought is "I will go to see my lawyer." The result is that the legal profession has as a major concern people who are in need of marital adjustment. While there may be some lawyers competent to handle such matters, even those among them most jealous of the rights of their profession will admit that as a whole they are not equipped to handle the problem adequately. A good number of them might also admit how valuable a course on marital counseling would be as part of the equipment of lawyers for the practice of their profession.

Every judge who sits in a domestic relations court will attest that if the machinery were provided for full and adequate marriage counseling, legal proceedings could be avoided. A court hearing is a traumatic experience. It must leave its mark on the parties even if there be a reconciliation.

On the whole the job of the judge in these cases is a frustrating one. He does not have the time to work with the parties even if he were personally equipped to do marriage counseling. For the most part he is attempting to divide a salary of fifty to seventy-five dollars between husband and wife and children living apart, leaving both parties with insufficient moneys, bitter, and resentful. Too many respondents fall into arrears and are brought back time and again and adjudged in contempt. Some are sent to jail. In custody cases the judge has seldom the problem of choosing between right and wrong. In most cases it is choice between two rights or two wrongs. Sometimes the fight is really over who should get the proceeds from public assistance following custody of the children. Frequently the judge realizes that neither parent is adequate and his only alternative is to leave the children with the one who will do the least harm. One might justifiably feel that far from bringing many of the parties together, the legal process separates them further.

Is marriage counseling the full answer to the problem? It can only be an answer in the relatively few cases which the present number of counselors and facilities can reach. Improving the present legal process by providing more trained marriage counselors would help. The only real solution is a program of prevention. This should start long before the marriage takes place. The schools must provide education for marriage. A part of the education will necessarily have to be that it is not a disgrace to consult someone when trouble arises. Too many couples are ashamed to admit their failure and only do so by resorting to law when it is almost too late to repair the damage. Public marriage counselors will have to be provided, separate and apart from the courts. A good place would be at the marriage license bureau. Couples might more readily go to the place where authority for the marriage was given to discuss their problems. They may not go there with the same joy when they applied for their license, but at least they could go there with some sense of dignity and without the feeling of failure and shame they carry with them when they come to court. Only a program of prevention, one that will make the legal process unnecessary, is the hope of the future, if we are to prevent the tremendous waste of human energy, degradation, and hardship that is now the fate of too many maladjusted married couples.

Part Two
The Moral Climate of Marriage

Chapter 12

The Protestant Point of View on Sex, Marriage, and Divorce

EDWIN E. AUBREY, B.D., Ph.D.

THE Protestant point of view on marriage is understood best, I think, against the background of the medieval Catholic view from which it departed. In the history of the institution of marriage, the Middle Ages represent a period of continuing tension between the mores of Roman Christian and the Teutons, and during the Reformation, the Teutonic mores of the northern Germanic tribes tended to reassert themselves. In other words marriage, which had been originally regarded as a mutual civil agreement among the Teutons, changed steadily under increasing control by the church. You can actually trace this in terms of the geographical location of the place of the wedding. The early Teutons simply made their own arrangements and were forthwith married. Then the church sent a priest to bless the marriage, then the couple were persuaded to come to the door of the church to receive the blessing of the priest upon the marriage. Eventually they were brought inside and the marriage consecrated, which came to be regarded as a sacrament of the church.

The Protestant reformers revived the view that marriage is a civil contract and not one of the seven sacraments. In reducing the sacraments from seven to two, they left out the sacrament of marriage, at the same time regarding it, of course, as of profoundly religious significance.

The Anglican Church, which was not as deeply affected by the German Reformation as other branches of Protestantism, has in these matters stayed somewhat closer to the Roman Catholic Church, and we shall see the effects of this upon their attitudes on matters of contraception and divorce. One of the major contributions, if you may call it such, that the Reformation made to the whole conception of marriage was in its attack on celibacy. The Catholic Church had taken the view, which St. Paul had advocated, that if one could not remain continent then he had better marry or, as Paul said, "It is better to marry than to burn." This made marriage at least a second best; and, indeed, Paul said in another place that he wished his readers were all as he was, that is to say, unmarried; but that if they could not be that, then they could marry.

Hence the tradition that came down through Christianity and was strongly expressed in Medieval Catholicism, with its conception of the superiority of the "religious," that is, those belonging to the monastic orders, was that celibacy was a higher order of life than marriage. Against this view John Calvin, the reformer, lodged a definite and vigorous protest. He said that the dignity of marriage was so diminished, and its sanctity so obscured, that he who did not refrain from marriage was not considered as aspiring to perfection with sufficient fortitude of mind.

To this view, then, Calvin lodged his objection, and the Protestants accepted marriage as an ordinance of God, for the good of society, and married couples as agents of God for the achievement of His purpose. This meant that in Protestantism marriage was regarded with utmost seriousness, but that its enjoyment was understood in terms of its being a contribution to the creative activity of God in the world, so that the creativity of sex was one way of expressing the cooperation of man with God in His creative work in the world.

Another aspect of the Reformation that has to be borne in mind in order to understand Protestantism is that the Protestants returned from the authority of the church per se to the authority of the Bible, and particularly to the authority of the New Testament. Now in this matter Luther, himself, was somewhat ambivalent. There were times when he declared the authority of the New Testament to consist in the fact that it carried the message of salvation by faith, and he was therefore not too much concerned with the literal details. When, however, he was confronted with certain proposals for communistic sexual union, in some of the experiments in the Anabaptist communities, he opposed them with extreme vigor, and in these cases tended to return to the Bible as specifying regulations governing human sexual life.[1]

Paul, then, with his low estimate of marriage was not followed in this regard, as he was in so much of the rest of Luther's thinking. Luther, himself, after his break with the church, married, and the woman he married was one who had fled from a convent. Many of the objections of the reformers were based upon the scandalous abuses that existed in the monasteries and nunneries as the result of the attempt to suppress the sexual life. And over and over again you find, on reading Luther's letters, the protests against the licentiousness that characterized some of these medieval monasteries. This is not to say that the Catholics were not themselves seeking to reform the situation. Such efforts were vigorously made, but the reformers felt that the extreme view that Roman Catholicism had adopted had produced more problems than it solved.

To turn to the contemporary situation in Protestantism, it must be borne in mind that there is no authoritative, official position

[1] Despite common opinion to the contrary, the Puritans later contended for the enrichment of marriage by mutual satisfaction in sexual intercourse. This has recently been brought to light by Professor M. Frye in an article in *Studies in the Renaissance*, vol. 2, pp. 148–59, 1955.

that can be stated for the Protestant view of marriage. We have nothing corresponding to papal encyclicals on this matter, which are normative for the thinking of the Catholic clergy, for we have no such centralized authority for Protestant ministers. We have in Protestantism two somewhat different attitudes in regard to sex and marriage.

Among more conservative Protestants the definition of marriage is that accepted in Roman Catholicism; that is, that the purpose of marriage is the procreation and rearing of children. That is its prime and important function. Ideas of companionate marriage, therefore, are not included in this view. Children are regarded as a blessing granted by God, and if it pleases God to give children to the union, then no opposition should be offered to the divine will in these matters; and for this reason some conservative Protestants will oppose contraception. Since they regard marriage as a life-long union, they would also be opposed to divorce, except for extreme reasons. Biblical literalism here takes them back to the saying of Jesus which, though recorded in two different Gospels, appears in only one context—that there should be no divorce except for adultery.

In many conservative Protestant groups, therefore, all other grounds of divorce are rejected. They would also insist that since the family is a part of what is called in Protestant theology the order of creation, that is, that it is divinely instituted and part of the ongoing work of the creation of the world, the family is to conceive itself as subordinate to the divine plan, and, therefore, that no family should be self-centered. The French sometimes speak of *egoisme à deux*, for which we have no English equivalent, that is to say, the mutual preoccupation of a married couple who see nothing beyond their own joint satisfaction and happiness. This view of the family would be rejected by Protestants, and certainly by those of the conservative group; and they would, for this reason, frown upon companionate marriage.

The liberal group represents a somewhat different approach. Instead of taking as literal authority the word in the Scripture about there being no basis for divorce except adultery, they take their point of departure from another aspect of the teaching of Jesus which pervades all of his message, and that is that institutions are made for man and not man to serve the institutions, or, as Jesus put it, "The sabbath is made for man not man for the sabbath." Professor Lichtenberger published in 1931 a monograph on divorce, and in listing the factors contributing to the increase in divorce in this country he included liberal Protestantism. His reason for doing this was that the liberal Protestant view that the institution exists to serve persons rather than the persons being subordinate to the institutions had a loosening effect upon the rigidity of thinking about divorce, for it meant that if a couple found that in the marriage their personalities were being thwarted or corrupted in one way or another, then the dissolution of the union would be, from the religious point of view, legitimate in the interest of the preservation of human personality.

With regard to sexual union in marriage the liberal Protestant view would be that this is to be regarded as a consummation of love. If you want to speak of it as a broader and more inclusive personal love—or if you want to use the term spiritual love—then sexual union is regarded as a supreme expression, though not the sole expression, of this love. This would indicate that the meaning of the act of sexual union is enriched by the total range of values which it expresses. The persons who engage in sexual union simply for the sake of finding a simple and crude physical outlet would be, from this standpoint, at the lowest level of sexual expression. Where two people seek mutual physical satisfaction as a part of the expression of their love for each other, this would be a higher expression of sexual life. But where they come to regard this as a common creative process, and to think of themselves as sharing in this creative power so that they can look to *our* child, *our* family, here the sexual union has itself become the occasion of a great enrichment of their life together, and of the meaning that they have for each other.

Furthermore, where there is a concern not merely for self-satisfaction or immediate mutual satisfaction but for the other as a total person, then the act of sexual union would be regarded as a part of the total fulfillment of the life of the other party to the union. Where this view is taken it is obvious that mutual satisfaction would be regarded as a part of satisfactory coitus. On the other hand it should also be mentioned that here the sexual union is regarded as a part of the merging that comes, so far as it is humanly possible, of two personalities; and it takes on not merely its immediate physiological significance but a larger symbolic significance which seems to the Protestant liberal to fulfill, therefore, a spiritual or religious purpose.

Thus the liberal Protestant would regard contraception as permissible not only on medical grounds (for example to protect the wife's health) but also perhaps to eliminate the fear of too many children, for where there is an economic problem of the proper rearing of children this fear might serve as a psychological obstacle to complete union, acting as a restraining force and thwarting, therefore, the complete consummation of the sexual act. At the same time he would not consider contraception as a threat of degradation. He would be well aware that psychologically speaking there is no sexual satisfaction except where there is mutual satisfaction in the sex act, and since this depends on mutual response anyway, the fear of contraceptives as a means of exploiting another person would cease to have much weight.

An indication of the way in which Protestant thinking has changed in recent years with regard to the problem of contraception may be found in the successive pronouncements of the Lambeth Conferences of Anglican Bishops (the nearest to a world-wide authoritative body in Episcopalianism). Meeting in 1908 the bishops made the following declaration: "The conference regards with alarm the growing practice of artificial restriction of the family and earnestly calls upon all Christian people to discountenance the use of all artificial means of restriction as demoralizing to character and hostile to national welfare."

In 1930, the attitude changed considerably, and this changed attitude would be useful, I think, in dealing with Protestants from the standpoint of religious scruples, for where it seemed in the opinion of the physician that contraception was indicated a statement like this would carry considerable weight: "The Conference emphasizes the truth that the sexual instinct is a holy thing implanted by God in human nature. It acknowledges that intercourse between husband and wife as the consummation of marriage has a value of its own within that sacrament and that thereby married love is enhanced and its character strengthened."

While they still recommended continence rather than the use of mechanical devices, they nevertheless permitted them.

I have already suggested the attitudes with regard to divorce: that it is permissible if marital happiness is impossible. It has to be recognized, of course, that the unhappiness may be due to causes other than the sexual factor, though it is quite possible that the sexual maladjustment might itself be an occasion for such a divorce. In dealing, then, with these attitudes, we must recognize that despite these differences, the Protestant feels that his Christian faith makes a contribution to the marriage relation by virtue of certain principles that it lays down, the first of which is respect for the person at the highest level of his possibilities. The theological phrase that every person is a "child of God" is intended to suggest that every person should be accorded full respect, and this would mean a total regard for the well-being of the other person. Therefore, in sexual relationships the total person should be thought of, and the individual regarded not merely as a possible avenue for sexual expression of the husband or of the wife.

The second point would be the recognition that every person develops not only in terms of his own capacities but also by reference to aims beyond himself. Much has been made in Protestant thinking of the doctrine of vocation, that is, that man is divinely called by God to the exercise of certain functions in the interests of society. Now this conception in Protestant thought has a much wider reference than simply the vocation of the ministry or one's professional occupation. It carries the connotation that marriage itself is a vocation for the enrichment of the lives of its participants and for the improvement of the community.

The third point would be the insistence that life whether in sex or in society is a sharing of differences, and that the Christian idea of unity is one of the sharing of difference so that the common life, whether in marriage or in the community, may be enriched. I would be inclined to say here that the Protestant might object to the idea sometimes expressed in Catholic teaching that it is of utmost importance that marriage be based on similarity. Quite apart from psychological considerations, the Protestant would hold that the differences that exist between the parties to a marriage may become occasions for the great enrichment of each and of their common life. This would mean that mere patience toward the peculiarities of the other should be transcended in a grateful recognition of the contributions that the differences may make to a fuller and richer understanding.

Finally, the Protestant would feel that since life is sometimes attended by disappointments where the couple want children and there are none, this frustration can be met by sublimation; therefore that there are other satisfactions that may be sought, even where the sexual adjustment has not, itself, been fruitful.

When dealing with Protestant ministers, then, it is important to keep in mind which of the two types of Protestants they are. It is encouraging that increasing attention is being paid in the theological seminaries to the relations between religion and psychiatry and religion and psychological counseling, with no attempt, fortunately, to develop amateur psychiatrists, but rather to enable ministers to detect problems of serious psychological maladjustments and to see that the parishioners who suffer from them get into the right hands. At the same time there is among ministers a growing concern with premarital counseling, with some very helpful work being done by them. It ought to be possible for the doctor and the minister to collaborate in these areas without entering into complications regarding professional ethics. The ministers may often have insight from their pastoral work that may be of great service to the doctor in dealing with a problem of marital adjustment. And where the two can come together in consultation, I think that there is promise of a very valuable enhancement of marriage in the modern world, and of the contributions of religion as well as of medicine to it.

Chapter 13

The Catholic Point of View on Sex, Marriage, and Divorce

A. H. CLEMENS, Ph.D.

TO OBTAIN the best results with Catholic counselees in marriage you will need to understand that the most important thing for them is to make available to themselves in increased quantities the grace of God. That is primary in our belief of what religion contributes to marriage. We think that there is such a thing as a divine plan for marriage; we think this part of this plan is visible in the order of nature; we think that regardless of what religion or lack of religion a given individual may have, he can discover this part of the plan for marriage (which the author of nature and of marriage placed in nature) by observation, experimentation, and above all by the light of human reason. Accordingly we believe that marriage is basically a natural institution, one imbedded in nature. It would seem that the author of nature was as wise as the average human inventor of an automobile or refrigerator; the latter always lays down certain rules for the proper use of the instrument he has invented. These God-made laws we like to call natural laws. Furthermore, we also think that marriage is a sacrament, that it has been elevated to a supernatural level (above nature) by virtue of its becoming a sacrament. If we study the plan of Providence found in the laws of nature, the goals, the structures, and the functions of marriage become quite clear. However, these purposes are quite controverted in our present-day cultural milieu. We conceive of them as being first social—*viz.*, the question of the generation and education of children—and second personal—*viz.*, companionship, mutual assistance, sex expression, love, development of personality (and not excluding the development of one's religious and moral personality). We further believe that here above all first things should be kept first and that the order of nature's purposes should never be inverted.

The first goal is clearly a social one, since it implies a contribution to society; the second one we conceive of as being an individual purpose. These are not unlike purposes that we find in the order of nature elsewhere. Food, for instance, has the purpose of keeping an individual alive, of self-preservation; that is the first purpose of food which we all recognize. The pleasure of eating we also admit to be a purpose of eating but entirely subordinate to its chief objective, which is to keep oneself alive. All of us find it quite revolting to read about the decadent Romans of antiquity going to banquets, gorging themselves with a meal, and then tickling their throats with a feather to bring up that meal in order to eat a second repast. There is something very revolting to our natural sensibilities about that fact, because there is something unnatural about the use of food exclusively for pleasure. In like fashion the preservation of the human race is the first goal of marriage and sex, with the other purposes subordinate to it. We do recognize the second goal as a very legitimate one when it in no way frustrates the overriding first purpose.

We also think, of course, that marriage is built on love and sex, and rightfully so. But to us sex is associated with the love of two personalities. We do not think that sex should be conceived of as a physical act, exclusively, or even as a physical fact predominantly. Rather, we think that love and sex both are a union of two total human personalities. These personalities we conceive as consisting of a will, an intellect, a set of emotions, and a body.

To us sex means the merger of all four of these levels of the human personality and not just one. Furthermore we think the genesis of love and sex attraction is on the intellectual level because one can hardly love what he does not know. We think that it then progresses to the will (an individual wants what he has come to know) and that there is a spontaneous overflow of the volitional to the emotional and physical levels. It is, therefore, quite natural that one should fall affectionately in love and quite natural, also, that there be a physical response in love. But we do believe with complete conviction that love and sex consist of all four of these levels of personality in operation. Therefore, we think that in sex adjustment in marriage, the important thing is not physical union. Good or bad physical adjustment, to us, is merely an end result; it is a symptom and not an isolated fact in itself. Rather, we think that sex adjustment or sex maladjustment is indicative of factors operative particularly on the upper two levels and possibly on the third level of the human personality.

A phenomenon such as frigidity, we believe, is mostly psychological. Scientific studies verify this. We do not find it difficult to explain why women are becoming more frigid by "degrees" (meaning higher degrees in education) or why those who know more of the facts are more frigid than those who know less. We find this very easy to explain in the light of our concepts of human personality. We think that the Biblical expression "two in one flesh" is just the beginning of the concept that religion gives us of marriage. Because it really is not just two in one flesh. Even more is it (as our modern culture would have it be) two hearts that beat as one. We think more profoundly that it is two intellects that see as one and two wills that "want" as one.

So we are opposed to mixed marriages of any kind whether they be cultural, social, religious, or otherwise. Any type of mixed marriage, we feel, interferes with the possibility of plumbing the depths of union inherent in a marriage. If marriage is to be a complete merger on all four levels, it calls for the highest degree of similarity on all those levels. Only then can the maximum merger be effected; only then can we speak of two people being one, to such extent that they almost lose their identity. We believe, for instance, that when St. Paul says "The man who hates his wife and puts her aside hates himself," he is speaking about a unity in marriage so profound that the human mind cannot grasp it. He is speaking in terms of identity. Yet we do not believe that the individual personality loses its autonomy in marriage. Here we are faced with a natural mystery: how the individual personality can remain autonomous and yet merge itself so profoundly in another personality that we can speak of the two being one. This remains a natural mystery, but it does point out the profundity and depth of unity in marriage. Therefore, we think that marriage is characterized by its very nature with permanency which is implied in a deeply profound unity of the type we have been discussing.

The plan that we think God has for sex flows from the basic concept that it is the union of two total personalities on all four levels. Briefly summarized, it might be portrayed something like this. We, of course, believe in the fall of man in the Garden of Eden as being a truth, not a myth. We believe that before this fall, Adam and Eve—the two then existing human beings—enjoyed sex with an intensity of pleasure that we today cannot enjoy. Their senses, their emotions, and their intellect were more perfect than ours are. We also think that before the fall, their sex instincts were completely under the control of higher nature—intellect and will. And we think that with the fall, we lost some of the keenness of our intelligence and of our emotions and of our sex appetite. Hence the pleasurableness of sex has been reduced. But more important than that, we think that a great deal of control over sex has been lost also with the fall of man in the Garden of Eden. At the present it is observable that we do not at all times

have the ability to control sex impulses automatically through
the use of intellect and will. Such impulses sometimes come without our bidding and remain against our desire.

This is basic in the Catholic position on sex education. It is
the reason why we believe in giving sex education in such a way
that while all the necessary facts are presented to the individual,
those facts are given in such a way that they do not incite the
individual unnecessarily. Nor is he given unnecessary facts, because we are conscious that this is an individual who has a weak-
ened will and a darkened intellect and a set of emotions over
which he does not have autocratic control. Therefore, the unnecessary portrayal of facts—and I emphasize the word *unnecessary*—can have only one possible result, *viz.*, to stimulate an
individual who does not have complete control over his lower
appetites and to tempt him unnecessarily. This is our approach to
sex education. This is why we do not think that sex education
should consist exclusively in physical facts but also in attitudinal
formation and in the discipline of one's emotions. Such education is moral as well as informative.

Furthermore, we think that sex properly used in marriage is
a good thing, that it is noble, dignified, elevated, beautiful,
virtuous. We think it is an act of religion, mind you. We think,
furthermore, that its proper use has so much of a religious implication that it actually increases in the user the grace of God
and makes him more Godlike. Anything less than this we believe
is an insult to the creator of sex. He made it good. It was one
of the things that He made during the first seven days of creation.
As the Bible relates the story, on the seventh day He rested and
looked over it all and said it was very good. He did not except
sex—and neither do we. We believe that sex is good because it
is made by the Creator and because it serves a very lofty purpose. We recognize it as being a union of personalities which
has the purpose of keeping the human race alive. We see sex as an
expression of love and an intensification of love. More than

that, we believe that it is an imitation of Christ loving His Church.

We conceive of sex on three levels. We think a person can employ sex either as an animal, as a human being, or as a Christian. The animal level of sex is what it means to the elephant, to the bees, and to the birds. If it is in addition an emotional, intellectual, and volitional union, it is sexual union as a human being. But if it is a Christian union, sex being used by two people, both of whom have been baptized and who have grace of God with them, it is something more than just a human act.

Our whole concept of marriage and sex is a triangular one —husband, wife, and God. We think that God is a third partner to every marriage. We can conceive, therefore, of sex and marriage being an adjustment not just of husband and wife but more of husband and wife to something beyond either or both. Here is where I suppose we Catholics differ with a great many counselors throughout the nation who are not of our religious persuasion. At least if one can judge from current literature, the treatment of adjustment in marriage (whether it is sexual adjustment or psychological adjustment) is heavily weighted with the concept of relationships between husband and wife. In fact it is entirely a discussion of how to get this man and this woman to adjust to each other. But is this marriage? We think not. Marriage is something beyond both those partners and to which both of them must adjust. And I gather from the available literature that there is little if anything said of the need for husbands and wives to adjust to marriage. It seems entirely a question of John learning how to adjust to Mary and Mary learning how to adjust to John, oblivious of the fact that perhaps John in his adjusting to Mary may be adjusting to something in Mary that is destructive. From our point of view, both of them must adjust to something outside of marriage, and that something is the pattern of marriage and family in accord with the plan of God.

We think, too (and this I would like you to follow with some care, because I may not find it easy to explain clearly), that

while not all marital breakdowns can be traceable to the absence
of religious influence in the living of the husband or the wife,
the overwhelming majority of them can. Let me illustrate what I
mean by an example. To our way of thinking there are two religious moral virtues that are very basic in the interrelationship
that marriage is. One is the virtue of humility, which is defined
as the capacity for facing facts. The other is the virtue of charity,
which we all understand as being love of someone else. Now,
we believe that it is only the humble person who can ever come
to know himself, because it is only the humble person who is
willing to accept all the facts of himself including the unpalatable
ones. If all potential counselees accepted the unpalatable facts
about themselves, you and I would not need to labor trying to
structure them in marriage counseling to bring them around
gradually to accepting these facts. If they were not proud or
perhaps had an emotional blind spot or blockage, we would not
need to structure them and, therefore, we would not need to
counsel them. On the other hand we think you cannot know anyone else fully, completely, and accurately except through charity.
It is only through charity, it must be repeated, that accurate
knowledge of our fellow human beings is possible. Were partners
in marriage humble and charitable, they would know themselves,
they would admit their own shortcomings and defects, they would
accept the unsavory qualities they have in themselves, and they
would understand their spouse more fully.

Because of these two factors operative in the interpersonal
relationship that marriage is, we would have few counselees, I
suspect, to counsel, unless they be neurotic, psychopathic types
who should be referred to a psychiatrist in most instances. Now,
I cite this to illustrate the point I tried to make originally, that
if religious-moral virtues such as these were operative in marital
and family living, we would have a much smaller incidence of
marriage breakdown. And I would relate this to sex in marriage.
I think any two people in marriage approaching the sex act with

humility and with charity will avoid, as I understand it, the two big shoals of sexual maladjustment—frigidity (usually on the part of the female) and impetuosity, haste, lack of consideration, and impulsiveness (on the part of the male). Both of these difficulties I suspect are traceable to either a lack of humility or charity or both in a great many instances, though perhaps not in all instances. So I think that the influence of religion in marriage is extremely basic, profound, fundamental, and far-reaching in its implications.

I should like to revert to the point with which I opened, that all of this gives us sets of attitudes (and by and large our human conduct is an external expression of an internal attitude of mind). If these attitudes are genuine, (given no abnormal, psychological conditions in either spouse) they should transfer themselves into conduct. But these attitudes give rise to expectations, and this I would like to emphasize (for I think if it is not the most fundamental, it is close to being so): that marriage, used subjectively, not objectively from God's standpoint of marriage but subjectively in the sense of whether I will be happy in marriage, make adjustments easily, find peace and harmony in it or not, will in a very large measure depend upon the expectancy with which I go into marriage. Often, it appears, people suffer in the throes of maladjustment for no other reason than that they went into marriage with completely different sets of expectations; these came from different sets of attitudes which in turn in large measure arose from their religious convictions. In addition, these expectations flow from ethnic group culture; they are associated with class structure; they are associated with a great many other sociological phenomena.

But over and above all this, religion gives us motivation, and I do not think this is its least important contribution. Our religion still teaches that on the one hand there is a hell and on the other that it is just as hot as it ever was. We do not think that hell has been air-conditioned, in spite of modern inventions, and we believe that this is a strong motive. When other motives fail, we think this motive of fear, salutary fear, wholesome fear (not a phobia in the pathological sense of the word) is a good emergency brake. But the other motive that we much prefer (we do not prefer to use the emergency brake; we hope that the regular brakes will work), that other motive is a positive one: it is the love of God; it is the strong desire to grow in holiness and sanctity, to become more Godlike by living out God's plan, in the ultimate hope that if we so lead our lives, heaven will be the final reward. Now, whether you believe in heaven or hell, your Catholic counselees do. These are effective motivations on the conscious level. Effective, did I say? I would say the strongest possible motivations that any human being can have on the conscious level are the love of God on the one hand and the fear of hell on the other.

So I would summarize in this fashion. Religion's influence is observed through its teachings, through its graces, through the attitudes and expectations that it gives to married couples, through the motivation that it gives, through helps, both supernatural and natural. And I would like to end on this note—that this influence being exercised by our religion is a rightful influence being constantly and more and more confirmed by the modern scientific studies in the field of marriage and the family that emanate from our research laboratories.

Chapter 14

The Jewish Point of View on Sex, Marriage, and Divorce

RABBI DAVID H. WICE, D.D., D.H.L.

THE Jewish people carry an experience and an accumulated wisdom that have been handed down to us for about thirty-four centuries. To go to the Bible as a source book of Judaism is to go only to the "baby book" of Judaism. It is the foundation, the literary remains of about a thousand years of search for the interpretations of the laws of life and man's relationship to God and the universe. But one who knows the Bible thoroughly would still be twenty-one hundred years behind the times, in the interpretations and the adjustments of Judaism to its environment and to its changing thought and practice. There is a vast body of literature which is authoritative in Judaism, and it is important for us to remember that this literature is also important if we would trace Judaism's quest for truth. We have more than a hundred names for God—one of them is Truth—and as we seek after Truth and new knowledge and adjust our thinking to the finest that man has been able to conceive, we feel that the change is in itself a virtue. While there have been attempts in all these thirty-four centuries to crystallize and write down these truths into codes, the codes themselves become antiquated from time to time. In order to know the latest interpretation, according to Judaism, one must go to the early records, beginning with the Bible and continuing to the Talmud, but following the interpretations and codes throughout the centuries. Some of our practices are still in process of change.

Acculturation has its influence in Jewish practice. "Life is stronger than theology." What the people do and what they will accept ultimately become the norm in Judaism rather than the teaching of any individual. The fact that Judaism is predicated not upon the life or teachings of any one individual but is the accumulated wisdom of many, many men and women who have lived in many civilizations and cultures over many centuries is in itself the basis of its diversification.

It is interesting that in Hebrew we have no word for marriage as a concept. The wedding ceremony takes its name from the bridegroom. It was a vestigial remnant of the days when the groom was the important part of the ceremony. The word we use for marriage is "kiddushin," holiness or sanctity. Judaism believes that everything in life can be either debased or elevated by our attitudes toward it and the way we use or abuse it. We say that you have to eat to live but that that is the animal function. In Judaism we wash our hands before we eat, we thank God for the food we have, and we share it with the hungry—that is kiddushin, sanctity. We utter a blessing over wine because the Bible says that "wine rejoices the heart of man," but the Talmud says that when you drink you feel like an animal. Drink a little and you feel like a lamb; drink a little more and you feel like a lion; but if you keep at it you will feel like a monkey and then a pig—in other words preaching and teaching a certain golden mean, not total abstinence nor vulgar excess but rather the proper use of everything in life.

We know that the love of a man and a woman is natural. It can be abused and it often is. But Judaism says that when a man and a woman say to each other "Enter into kiddushin with me, into sanctity or holiness, so that out of this relationship (which we renounce with the rest of the world) we will find physical, emotional, and spiritual fulfillment and out of our fulfillment we will be able to build together the kind of home where it will be safe for children to be born and reared in love and security"—that is marriage.

We believe in the purity of family life. Once a man and woman have said to each other "Enter into kiddushin with me" (and that happens to be the formula of marriage) then it is their responsibility to have a family. Birth control not only was permissible in Judaism but under certain circumstances was mandatory—namely, to protect the health of the mother and the welfare of the family.

This goes back to codes that are more than two thousand years old. I would not recommend that you follow the procedures outlined in those codes—they used sponges and various other mechanical devices, referred to in these early codes, but as in everything else connected with Judaism, we say accept the principle out of the religious tradition but go to the best science of your day for the application. This concept may be found expressed in a book that dates from about the year 200 B.C. The book is Ecclesiasticus, found in the Apocryphal literature, where the person who is ill is given advice. He is told to set his affairs in order, to pray, to bring a sacrifice, to do penance, *and call the doctor!* That is, I believe, as good an answer of religions to cults of healing that leave the physician and scientist out of account as one can find in literature.

It is interesting that Judaism permits the woman to practice birth control but not the man. The teachers based this upon the Biblical verse (as everything in Judaism has to be based upon some word or phrase or thought expressed in Scripture, in the thirty-nine books of the so-called Old Testament). By interpretation they nullify laws which they felt no longer applicable. They could not erase the words from Scripture because they had been canonized, but they could be reinterpreted. The verse that is the basis of much of Jewish law pertaining to marriage and sex laws consists of the two words *Peru u' revu,* Be ye fruitful and multiply. In the Hebrew they happen to be in the masculine imperative form of the verb; therefore they said that *men* must be fruitful and multiply, but the women did not have to be!

In premarital counseling I usually tell young couples that though the law gives the woman the right to determine when she will become a mother and how often, I recommend highly that they consult on the decision.

Judaism, also basing its teaching upon that verse, says that until a couple has had two children, they have not fulfilled their marital obligation. It is interesting that in many cultures the exact number of children considered to be desirable or the minimum required, according to that culture, is clearly expressed. I remember once reading in a source book on education the Catechism of Napoleon, which he had prepared for the French people in the last years of the eighteenth century. The first question in the Catechism was: "How many children does a French family have to have?" The answer was: "Six—one to replace the father, one to replace the mother, one to fight for Napoleon, and three in case anything happened to the first three." Now in Judaism we know that in the long course of the centuries our families varied with the times, conditions, economic factors, political milieux, and environment, but almost universally the Jewish birth rate has been lower than the population among whom the people lived at any particular time. A Jewish family in the twentieth century in Yemen (southern Arabia) may have an average of ten children, but those ten children are far fewer than the Mohammedan neighbors of those Yemenite Jewish families. And here in the United States the birth rate among Jews is lower than in the general population. It is interesting that the rabbinical authorities, recognizing birth control in our own time, dated the Responsum to the questions of the layman in 1927, but as the author of that article, Dr. Lauterbach, points out, the people have been practicing it for centuries. It is high time that we found in our codes and writings the historic thread by which they came to that conclusion.

In Judaism, we are against celibacy. Celibacy is a sin. A person has no more right to renounce sex than he has to commit suicide. Sexual expression is part of our birthright, and all that Judaism asks is that it be placed under moral restraint, under the moral law, under kiddushin, the sense of sanctity. There is a wholesomeness and a healthy-mindedness with regard to sex. It is interesting that when the Jewish child is circumcized, at the eighth day, the benediction recited at that ceremony is: "May this child live to his fulfillment in religious education, to a marriage worthy of our people, and to a life of fulfillment and good deeds." In other words even at the age of eight days we are looking toward the time when this individual will be able to fulfill his obligations. In older periods of our people's history it was decreed that a woman might remain unmarried if it was her fate. It was no sin for her to be single, on the assumption that she would marry if she could. But a man was required to get married by the time he was twenty and remain married until he was sixty. In other words widowers were required to remarry. Now, of course, that has changed with times and places. We know that because of the lengthened period of education and the necessity for some economic stability, in this country, for instance, marriage is often delayed. Yet there is still a carryover from the earlier sociological concepts of Judaism to the present time, and you will find that the marriage maker, the *Shadchan,* is still an institution among many of our people, even here in the United States. Early marriage is encouraged, even if it requires subsidizing by the families of the young man and woman. We regard this as one answer to the problem of the biologic sex urge. We consider this to be one way to solve the problem of juvenile delinquency and premarital or extramarital relationships.

Judaism frowned upon but never forbade divorce. If divorce was indicated after a careful study, the Talmud said that "it is better for four people to be happy than for two people to be miserable." (Of course, again, you see there the assumption that the couples would immediately remarry.) Far from frowning upon the remarriage of one who had been married and divorced, Judaism said the purpose of the divorce was to put this person into the condition where he could remarry and normalize or stabilize his life. This is still practiced among our people. There were social controls and there was public opinion, which limited the number of divorces, and the rabbis never made it easy, particularly if there was an adverse effect upon children. But because of the tensions of the incompatibility of couples, divorce was not only permitted but even made easier by the rabbis who controlled divorce as well as marriage. In the United States among traditional Jews marriage and divorce still are *religious* matters normally. In the reform groups divorce is regarded as a civil matter. Once the couple has been divorced, if they get a marriage license, they may remarry, though among traditionalists they must have an ecclesiastical divorce as well as the civil one to be eligible to remarry.

In the matter of sex taboos in childhood, masturbation is one of the classic examples according to the Biblical and Talmudic sources, the principle being that the seed is sacred for the continuation of life. I am sure that Kinsey is correct in his evaluation that masturbation is found so infrequently in the Jewish group. He says that those who adhere to the traditions of orthodox Judaism least frequently resort to masturbation as a sexual outlet, and they are least frequent in premarital and extramarital relationships. Certainly marriage teachings in the literature and the training of the individual have been important in this regard. Because of acculturation you will find many of the American Jews following the mores of their groups, according to education and economic interest, in an environment in which they can participate wholeheartedly. In other words, according to the Kinsey study, we know that there are great differences in sex practices among those who have finished high school as contrasted to those who have gone on and had a university education. And I am certain that this is also true in the Jewish group. The things that were learned by Jews in the universities affected them exactly as they did the non-Jews in the same group, and these have had a stronger hold upon the present generation of American Jews than some of the religious traditions. But this, too, is in good Jewish tradition, namely, the adaptation and adjustment of the individual to the time and place in which he lives, provided that nothing within the culture is contrary to the teachings of the religous group itself. In other words adultery is frowned upon in Jewish teaching and morality, and even though the practice should become popular in the community, Jewish teaching would never sanction it. This illustrates the differentiation between the fundamentals of religious law and what we might call the practices and mores and customs that grow out of the environment.

When physicians treat a Jewish patient, they can be assured that whatever is scientifically sound will be acceptable to him, unless he is motivated more by hearsay and superstition than by religious teachings. And you can put it down as a rule that some people will give up their religion before they will give up their superstition. A person who is truly religious may, for instance, ask for an interpretation by a religious teacher or a rabbi before permitting a postmortem examination. We know that there are statements in the Jewish code forbidding postmortem examination, and yet there is a Responsum today on the part of conservative and reform rabbis and statements by orthodox rabbis that if the postmortem examination will help to prolong the life of another person for even an hour, the postmortem is not only allowed but, again, becomes mandatory. For one of the great laws of Judaism is that you may break any other law in order to save a life. That is why, in the codes, Jewish physicians were told that they might help a sick person even on the Day of Atonement. There are many examples of health laws in Judaism that might interest the reader. A pregnant woman may not fast, for instance, even on fast days. A bride may not fast even on the Day of Atonement in her first year of marriage, for her chief function in that year is to keep herself beautiful and attractive and lovable. These are healthy-minded, practical-minded, wholesome-minded attitudes, and the Jew never regarded sex as something taboo or something to be shunted away. It was fundamental in the education of our children from the earliest times. We talked about it; we tried to be as normal and healthy-minded about it as we could. We regard sex as part of our nature. We have never made the dichotomy between good and evil. We say that all is part of one creation, part of the universe. It is our responsibility to curb the evil inclination, to guide it by moral law, and to cultivate that which we consider to be the good impulses of our human nature. We do not deny the existence of evil, but we would curb and direct that which might be evil within man.

I would conclude by making the fundamental statement that the Jew is basically healthy-minded toward sex and open-minded toward science and truth. This accounts for the fact that never in the last twenty-five centuries has there been illiteracy or ignorance among the Jewish people. There was no greater social stigma than illiteracy. Out of this literacy, out of this study, out of this quest for knowledge and the cultivation of the mind and heart have come an open-mindedness to the discovery of new truths. Medical science will find in the Jewish patient a great cooperator.

Part Three

Mating and Mismating

Chapter 15

Sexual Adjustment before Marriage

WILLIAM L. PELTZ, M.D.

I N ORDER to understand the sexual behavior of young people during their courtship and engagement, a consideration of various aspects of their adjustment prior to that time is necessary. It is well recognized today that attitudes toward sex and sexual behavior before marriage are determined not only by the current situations in which the young people find themselves but by many aspects of their early life, their cultural surroundings and their religious teachings, as well. Adolescence in particular and the years until marriage constitute periods of conflict for every young person. The growing desire of the boy or girl to be independent comes up against the restrictions of family and society, as well as the dependent needs stemming from within. Likewise there is conflict between the strong biological sexual urge which is reinforced in adolescence and the inhibiting effect of the mores and religous teachings (see Chapters 12, 13, and 14). Attempts at resolution of the conflict are varied and many.

Some young people remain more or less abstinent, others make compromises of one sort or another, and others indulge themselves quite freely. With the intensification of emotions and desires prior to marriage, some physical expression of sexuality, whether in the form of kissing, petting, or intercourse, is to be expected and, within certain limits, may even be considered normal and desirable as a prelude to later adjustment. What these limits are to be for the young person is a question about which there is no complete agreement. People differ markedly in their opinions on the subject depending upon their own experiences, prejudices, moral codes, and sense of values.

Ideally, there is a natural or normal progression from the time of puberty to the time of marriage. If a child of fourteen or fifteen is sexually precocious or, on the other hand, if a person of thirty has never dated the opposite sex or experienced sexual sensation, something has obviously gone askew in the process of natural physiological and emotional growth and development. The normal progression usually involves a shift from interest in members of one's own sex at the time of puberty to interest in members of the opposite sex within the next few years. There is usually a progression from autoerotic and possible homosexual activity to various degrees of heterosexual activity. Ideally, again, a person's emotional and sexual life unfolds gradually, with the result that by the time of engagement and marriage he has achieved a considerable degree of maturity and a corresponding increase in independence and sense of responsibility. In addition, temporary and constantly shifting infatuations have given way to more permanent and realistic relationships.

It is well to keep in mind that the sexual behavior of boys during the teen years and the years thereafter prior to marriage differs considerably from that of girls. Even though most boys mature sexually about a year later than girls, from then on for ten or fifteen years, they experience a more active sex life. During the teen years boys experience on the average about two orgasms a week, whereas girls do so far less frequently. Moreover, masturbation is almost universal among boys at some time or other. By way of example, for boys of the upper educational group (those who go through high school and beyond) masturbation, with fairly frequent nocturnal emissions and with occasional intercourse, is the most usual sexual outlet; for boys of the lower educational group (those who do not go as far as high school), on the other hand, the picture is very different. These boys usually give up masturbation fairly soon after it has begun and from then on have fairly frequent and regular intercourse prior to marriage. They disapprove of masturbation and find it hard to understand why a grown man should masturbate or stop at petting when intercourse is available to him. Males who enter but do not pass beyond high school have a sex life that lies between these two extremes. It has been found, too, that boys who mature early usually have a more active sex life than boys who mature later.

The sex life of girls differs from that of boys in various respects. In the first place they are aroused sexually less frequently and less readily and experience fewer orgasms. Sixty-two per cent of females of all ages in Kinsey's sample, for example, masturbated at some time in their lives. However, it occurred less frequently during the teens and increased with age, whereas in boys the incidence fell after reaching a peak at about age sixteen.[1] Next to petting, however, it was the form of sexual activity in which the largest number of girls engaged prior to marriage.

Masturbation is still condemned by many people on moral or religious grounds. Others maintain that "excessive" masturbation is physically harmful. (Rarely, however, do these people make clear what they mean by "excessive." They may not realize that it is quite normal for one boy to experience orgasm every day, whereas another may normally experience it once a week, once a month, or even less.) Because of the conflict between their sexual desires or activity on the one hand and their moral and religious codes on the other, millions of boys and girls, and men and women, too, experience anxiety and guilt when they masturbate. Such conflict and guilt may lead to emotional turmoil,

[1] Alfred C. Kinsey, Wardell B. Pomeroy, and Clyde E. Martin, *Sexual Behavior in the Human Male*, W. B. Saunders Co., Philadelphia, 1948.

difficulties in concentrating on studies or work, and interfere with efficiency and social adjustment. It should be pointed out that these symptoms are the result of the anxiety and worry stemming from the sense of guilt rather than from the masturbation itself. It is a medically accepted fact today that the act of masturbation is not harmful physically and that it does not lead to mental illness.

When boys and girls are in their early and middle teens, an interest in the opposite sex develops in the form of dating. This is a part of courtship in the broadest sense but is usually a prelude to "going steady" and to engagement. During these early years there is chiefly a competitive or narcissistic quality to dating. The desire to be successful and popular exists in both boys and girls and is acted out in the game of dating. But as Margaret Mead points out, "the game is cast in highly sexual terms." Parents take dating for granted and expect it of their children as a desirable phase of their growing up and learning to adjust to the world of reality. Almost complete freedom is given with the withdrawal of chaperoning, and yet premarital intercourse is disapproved of, pregnancy is a calamity, and abortion for illegitimate pregnancy is against the law. Consequently petting is the compromise which young people have made in an effort to resolve this dilemma.

Petting is described as any sexual activity up to but not including the act of intercourse. ("Necking" is always above whereas "petting" is either above or below the shoulders.) The topic of petting is one that is highly charged with feelings on the part of young people, their parents, and the community. Kinsey reports that during the past several decades premarital petting has become more frequent and has become elaborated as to the type and extent of activity engaged in. According to his figures about 90 per cent of the total male and female population engaged in some form of premarital petting before the age of twenty-five, with over a quarter of the males experiencing orgasm. It is far more frequent among boys and girls who go to high school or beyond than it is among those who do not go beyond grade school.

Petting that does not proceed to orgasm is not medically harmful but may lead to nervous tension or to pain. If orgasm does occur, there seem to be no aftereffects other than those following any other type of sexual activity. In spite of its prevalence and relative social acceptance, certain religious and moral codes are apt to condemn petting unless it is part of the foreplay of sexual intercourse in marriage. Thus premarital petting may lead to emotional conflict and guilt among those who engage in it. On the other hand it probably helps young people break down some of the inhibitions and restraints that develop during the early years of life, and thereby contributes to the effectiveness of sexual relations after marriage. Thus it has been suggested that perhaps the real importance of petting, over and above the relief from tension it provides, lies in the experience and education it offers in making sociosexual contacts.

Boys are expected not only to be the ones to seek the dates, but they are expected to ask the girls for as much as possible. Girls are expected to be courted but are also expected to be the ones who say no or otherwise set the limits. Whether intercourse does occur before marriage, then, is up to the girl. The boy desires it and often is expected to be active and aggressive in seeking it. He does everything possible to get the girl to say yes and is pleased not only physically but from the point of view of having mastered the situation when she does so. On the other hand he is taught culturally to idealize the girl who is virtuous, who says no, who preserves her virginity. These conditions are contradictory and often bewildering not only to the boy but to the girl as well. She wants to be popular and to be asked out on dates and so sometimes goes further than she realizes is discreet. And in doing so and in giving in for immediate popularity, she may lose the very esteem she so much desires.

It is but a hair's breadth between heavy petting and sexual intercourse, and the matter of premarital intercourse is a problem area that is apt to concern and worry young people before marriage. Its pros and cons are considered in open discussion groups and in counseling perhaps more frequently than any other question. It has been pointed out by students in the field that the question of premarital and extramarital intercourse has been a matter of social concern among all peoples throughout history, and that in nearly all cultures extramarital intercourse has been considered more disturbing than premarital intercourse. The matter of virginity in males is one of less concern in most cultures than that of females. Actually, most human males do have intercourse before marriage, with frequencies that vary between social levels even more than incidences do.

For the female we have Kinsey's figures [2] indicating that nearly half the women had intercourse before they were married, and that about half of this group confined it to the person whom they ultimately married. It is of interest that premarital intercourse (as well as masturbation and homosexuality) in both males and females occurred less frequently in the sample most actively involved with religious groups.

There is strong religious condemnation of premarital intercourse in our society and considerable public disapproval of it on moral or ethical grounds. However, the objections apply more to the woman, and especially to the young girl, than to the man. It is impossible to say on any scientific or quantitative basis what effect premarital intercourse has upon sexual adjustment or happiness in marriage. Instances can be cited to show that it leads to future difficulties; on the other hand other cases can be cited to show that it enhances the chances of a happy marriage. Some of the frequently stated disadvantages to premarital intercourse are the danger of pregnancy and of subsequent forced marriage

[2] Alfred C. Kinsey, Wardell B. Pomeroy, Clyde E. Martin, *Sexual Behavior in the Human Female*, W. B. Saunders Co., Philadelphia, 1953.

or abortion; the danger of venereal disease; the loss of self-respect, or of partner and respect; the possibility that the friendship or engagement may end as a result of guilt feelings; the effect of guilt upon marriage, whether to one's premarital partner or to someone else; the effects of infringement of a moral code and of disapproval by other people; the possibility that premarital intercourse will increase the likelihood of promiscuity and extramarital intercourse.

Some of the arguments in favor of premarital intercourse are the physical and psychological outlet and satisfaction; the possibility that it may relieve tension and frustration and thereby enable one to live more effectively; that it is preferable in some people's opinions to other forms of sexual outlet; that it may facilitate through experience the individual's physical and emotional adjustment in subsequent marriage; that it is one way of finding out if people who are in love will be able to adjust sexually after marriage; that it is easier to make adjustments when young than at a later age; that it is customary in certain groups.

Strong biases exist on both sides of the question, prejudice and the moral codes or value systems of the people concerned usually determining their viewpoints. Thus it is important for the counselor to have some knowledge of the cultural variations of the general concepts of "right" and "wrong" as well as of the development of the individual, his conscience or superego. Some people, for example, have what might be termed a "fundamentalist" point of view about right and wrong. They might maintain, by way of example, that certain forms of sexual activity prior to marriage are wrong from a moral or religious point of view. One such person might feel that any sexual activity before marriage is wrong; another might accept petting or masturbation but not premarital intercourse; and another might accept petting and intercourse but not masturbation. On the other hand other people look at the matter from a more relative or "humanistic" point of view, feeling that what is wrong for one person or group might be perfectly all right for another person or group. This is probably the attitude of most physicians and counselors whose aims are not to impose their own set of standards upon the people with whom they function professionally or to make them conform to any other particular code of ethics, but rather to help them attain competence or adequacy in their interpersonal relations.

A few special considerations of counseling relating to sexual adjustment before marriage should be mentioned. For example, some young people want help in deciding whether the girl should have her hymen dilated before marriage. Others are worried as to whether their previous sexual behavior was so abnormal as to constitute a perversion and therefore contraindicate their getting married or achieving satisfying adjustment in marriage. Still others wonder whether to confide in their partners about their previous sexual behavior.

As regards the question of having the hymen dilated, there are obvious advantages to this in terms of freedom from discomfort and avoidance of a possible physical obstacle to a satisfactory adjustment while on the honeymoon. Many people prefer to have this accomplished; others prefer to let nature take its course, usually because of their wanting to experience actual evidence of the girl's virginity. In counseling in these cases it is usually wise to discuss the matter not only with the girl but with her fiancé as well, especially if they have not already discussed the matter together, for it may turn out that the man's feelings on the subject are very different from the woman's.

Concern as to whether previous sexual experiences constitute a contraindication to marriage is most apt to apply to masturbation, homosexual activity, and venereal disease. Catharsis combined with education usually takes care of the problem of worry over masturbation. The same is true if the person is fundamentally heterosexually oriented but has had some experiences with members of the same sex during preadolescence or adolescence. During these years he was in the so-called homosexual phase of growing up and was frustrated in achieving a heterosexual outlet because of the usual restrictions that society imposes. Hence if he has progressed from the homosexual phase to the heterosexual, these previous experiences need not act as obstacles to sexual adequacy in marriage. On the other hand the situation in which there is cause for concern is when a person is embarking upon marriage in an effort to escape from a basic homosexual tendency. In such cases marriage is probably contraindicated, at least for the time being. When the worry is over previous venereal disease, the young person should be referred to a qualified physician.

Should young people who are planning to marry tell all of their former sexual experiences to their partners? Although in general it is desirable for each to come to know the other as thoroughly as possible and to share ideas, experiences, and feelings, the answer as to whether to confide depends upon many circumstances. For example, the personality of each partner as well as the degree of sharing, closeness, and mutual understanding that already exists in their relationship would make a considerable difference. For one thing the desire to share could actually represent a need to be relieved of guilt. For another, if such sharing occurred too soon, it could cause too much anxiety or otherwise be too upsetting to the partner. In some cases it is best to delay confiding. In other cases it is wise not to discuss the former experiences at all. It is probably best for the counselor to explore the possible advantages and disadvantages of sharing or not sharing these things rather than to suggest a course of action in the matter. Sometimes the counselor can be of help in discussing or interpreting the facts to the partner if the decision has been to confide.

Finally, there is the matter of suggesting reading to engaged couples about sexual adjustment before and after marriage and about other aspects of engagement and marriage. Such shared reading serves not only to acquaint the couple with useful and necessary information but also frequently serves another even more important function: it helps break down the barriers of reticence and inhibition that inevitably exist to some extent between all young people and thereby brings them into a closer relationship with each other. (See Appendix.)

In conclusion it may be re-affirmed that of utmost importance is a healthy sexual development which prepares the way for a conflict-free sexual relationship in marriage, a relationship that brings a couple closer together not only physically but spiritually; a state of closeness, togetherness or sharing rather than a state of narcissistic self-centeredness. But perhaps the most important thing of all is the determination to make the marriage succeed. Only with this and the willingness to do everything possible to make it succeed will young people achieve a happy and successful marriage.

Chapter 16

Sexual Partnership in Marriage

WILLIAM FITTIPOLDI, M.D.

THE family is a basic unit of contemporary society. Sometimes it serves as a breeding ground to foster the regressive tendencies of its members and mobilize neurotic interaction. The relationship of the husband and wife in the family determines, more than any other factor, whether the particular family unit is to be a breeding ground of pathology or of competence and health. In marriage there are inevitably problems. There is rarely such a thing as a sexual problem per se, but rather difficulties that show up in the area of sex or physical lovemaking. This part of marriage is the most instinctual in expression and the one most fraught with guilt, anxiety, tension, difference, argument, projection, blame, and shame. Psychologically and emotionally, marriage is an attempt at a partial fusing of two distinct personalities each of whom has lived a long time in his own way. Sex being the area of greatest *feeling* it will often be the presenting problem when there is marital conflict.

Purely for didactic purposes, I have attempted to classify sexual symptoms of marital difficulty into eight categories. The first is frigidity. The second is impotence. (These two problems are covered at greater length by Dr. English.) The third is frequency of sexual contact between the partners. Couples come for help with considerable confusion and concern about how often they should get together. Often there is a difference in desire between the two mates, most frequently with the male desiring more contact than the female. The fourth is extramarital contact in one or both mates. The fifth is the timing of orgasm. Even when mates agree on most other things they frequently have difficulty in reaching a reasonably spontaneous orgastic release. The sixth concerns the types of sexual activity—the various experimentations that occur in marriage. The seventh centers around child spacing and contraception, which are related to the eighth, namely, fear of pregnancy.

For the physician, the presenting complaint may not be a sexual one. People may come to the doctor's office with a variety of physical troubles. They may have tachycardia or gastric difficulty. They may have headaches or diarrhea. The psychosomatic or the physical symptoms referable to difficulty in marriage are multitudinous and not always easy to isolate. But if the marital problem is carefully appraised, one usually finds it is also showing up in some way in a disordered sexual life. Which comes first is an academic problem of little practical importance, as you will see from the cases I am going to present. Incidentally, the cases I have selected are those of *men,* and for a special reason. It has been my experience that men take their sexual troubles to physicians more readily than do women, and since the majority of physicians are men, a word of caution is called for. The male patient appeals to the male doctor with: "Doc, help me with my wife." Frequently, if you investigate the situation, the appeal should be: "Doc, help me with myself."

Typical of this approach was Mr. S, a thirty-year-old man who came to me referred by an astute local physician. His chief complaint was: "My wife is cold; she does not stimulate me enough." A careful history revealed that although he was capable of erection, he could not have orgasm after a full hour of penetration. Now this is probably beyond the average limit. It was not that he did not "want" to experience climax but that he could not. His orientation to the problem was that his wife was cold; she was not stimulating him enough. An interview with the wife revealed her to be warm, reasonably passive, well-adjusted, and feminine. Investigation of the couple's activities showed there was participation on the wife's part as well as diversity. Mr. S's problem, it became apparent, did not lie in the sexual sphere. Further interviews with him revealed him to be extremely self-centered, his entire orientation to women and to the sex act being one of greed and anger. He spoke constantly of what he was not getting out of the relationship. In the beginning of our work together, Mr. S had no awareness of the fact that it was possible to have an emotional openness to what the woman might want to experience. He was unable to consider his wife at all. He was so filled with anger and resentment, not only toward his wife but toward female figures in general, that he could not allow himself the amount of "giving" involved in the physical release of orgasm. Orgasm is an act of biological love, and love had nothing whatsoever to do with what he was attempting to do with his wife. In many ways he was unconsciously trying to hurt his wife in the sex act. Happily, a series of interviews helped him to realize what he was doing, and there was considerable improvement for both husband and wife. The point to be made about this case is that Mr. S might well have gone through a complete genito-urinary workup, needlessly wasting his time and money and the facilities of the already overburdened medical profession. He would have obtained no relief from his symptom if he had been treated on the basis of the manner in which he presented himself and his complaint.

The next case concerns Mr. D, a rather large, somewhat obese, athletic type of man about fifty years old. He was outgoing, extroverted, and apparently extremely well adjusted. He was sent to me at the request of his wife because of his periodic lack of sexual interest in her. Because of his age, a physician might look to involutional changes, since we are well alerted to the fact that men go through cyclic changes akin in many ways to the climacteric of women. He might look to endocrine modifications. However, I soon discovered the following chain of emotional events. Mr. D was reasonably successful in his own business, well known in the community, and liked and admired by most of his colleagues. His wife was a talented, highly successful interior decorator. However, whenever her income became greater than his, his masculinity became vexed. Feeling threatened, he would run away from his wife emotionally. He could not stand the fact that the wife could be, at least economically, the more powerful figure in the marriage. To bolster his threatened masculinity he would have extramarital affairs with "inferior" women. Between these escapades, however, Mr. and Mrs. D led a good, compatible married life. Mr. D was not at all aware of the motives for his behavior. He only knew that he was unhappy with these escapades. During therapy, he gradually became aware of the way he was using these other women and as a result rectified his behavior. Now my point about this case is that no amount of moralizing or chemical treatment could have helped him. He had to realize why he was doing what he was doing. These two examples and the one following illustrate the multitude of emotional factors that may come to be of importance in any sexual symptom of marital difficulty.

My third example is related to the timing of orgasm and the frequency of intercourse, a common complaint. Mr. R, thirty-seven years old, was doing well in the community. However, he was working in a highly competitive office situation and for twelve hours a day was under great tension, with the necessity of expressing a great deal of aggression in his everyday business contacts. He came to me with a rather typical masculine remark: "Doc, can you do something for my wife? She's frigid." When I talked with the wife I heard a different story. Mr. R would come home from work tense, irritable, cranky, and demanding. He spoke constantly of his anxiety about his work and of the competition involved. He expected and demanded intercourse every night. His usual period of penetration was less than one minute—which is considered premature ejaculation. Of course, the wife could obtain no sexual satisfaction, no orgastic release, although she was quite capable of this with adequate stimulation. As a result she was partially depressed and had headaches and other psychosomatic symptoms. She had not consulted a physician because she had what might be called an intuitive awareness of why she had these symptoms and, out of "faithfulness" to her husband, felt that she should not complain. The man was using what he thought was sex for an outlet for his own tension and anxiety. His wife's so-called frigidity was a result of his premature ejaculation, which in turn was a result of his work situation and tension.

Certain marital problems that find expression as dislocation in the sex life of the couple require special skills drawn from the field of marriage counseling or psychiatry. All of them, however, require an appreciation of the problems people have in living. One of the main questions calling for freedom from prejudice and blind spots in the helping person is that of what is normal in sexual behavior. Here the professional, whether clinician or counselor, should maintain an investigative and observing and genuine interest. It is generally believed in psychiatric circles that the ultimate aim in sexual behavior between male and female in marriage is to bring about the union of the genital parts of the body for spontaneous release. We also know from clinical investigation that people require a variety of forms of sexual behavior to complement the nuances of their instinctual and emotional needs. These contacts between parts of the body other than the genitals are normally part of the foreplay, yet they are veiled by taboo. The legal view of these expressions of sexuality has been to label them perversions, the laws regarding them dating back to the pre-Freudian era when little was known of sex psychology or physiology and a strong moralistic attitude linking sex with the baser side of man prevailed in religion. In some states, practices normally accompanying foreplay are considered legal grounds for divorce and sometimes for criminal action. In this regard, Kinsey comments that, depending on the type of activity, from 60 to 70 per cent of the college-bred population would be open to prosecution. Interestingly, the incidence of these activities among the lower educational levels is said to be correspondingly less. One might observe that the statement that the forms of behavior are related to degeneration hardly holds water.

What Kinsey learned for the broader population statistically, we have known generally in clinical practice for some years. There are people who require and desire a great deal of petting before actual penetration is made. To cite Kinsey again, he showed that there are substantial numbers of people who need as much as an hour of foreplay before entering into genital union.

Sexual experimentation relating to the following types of activity occurs widely in marriage. Mouth stimulation—type and degree of kissing, how long it should go on, how sensuous it should be—is usually the least tabooed practice. Next is breast stimulation, manually and orally. Then comes genital stimulation, manual, by one or both partners. Finally, there is contact between the genitals of one partner and the mouth of the other. Mouth-genital stimulation is still a rather taboo subject—as we will see from the case I am about to present. There is also a great deal of experimentation with positions for intercourse, particularly among young people, and related to this experimentation and sometimes going over into problems of a special nature are anal play and anal intercourse. Finally, there are two situations related to conflicts surrounding full participation in physical love, namely, masturbation by one or both partners, and homosexual trends in either partner. (See Chapter 18.)

Individuals with conflicts over the forms of sex play listed above come for help with a great deal of guilt, anxiety, and shame. How the person they come to handles them may have a profound effect on their lives. My own approach with such people is merely to cite the incidence of such activities. I do not condemn. I do not moralize. I do not tell them what to do. The dangers arising from interjecting a moralizing or legalistic atmosphere are dramatically illustrated in the following case.

Shortly after the marriage of a very personable young couple, active in the community, interested in church affairs, the husband sought some sexual exploration. He wanted to experiment with positions and variations of foreplay and expressed interest in oral-genital contact. The wife was quite naïve. Puzzled, she consulted the family physician, who told her that her husband was abnormal, branding him a pervert and urging her to seek a divorce. And so the marriage was terminated. On top of this, many people in the community heard of the grounds for the wife's action, resulting in his being ostracized and finally having to move to another city.

The physician who was consulted in this case was not psychiatrically trained and obviously not oriented to counseling. It is hoped that we, as professionals, can retain a clinical attitude, which implies an investigative interest in etiological factors. We should at least try to minimize moralistic or judgmental attitudes that might creep into our counseling with people who come to us with maladjustments or concerns in this area of their lives. Our own orientation to these problems will, inevitably, be determined by personal attitudes. Realization of our social, religious, and family training will color how we feel and think about the other person's sexual behavior. (See Chapters 12, 13, and 14.)

In closing I should like to offer some thoughts arising out of clinical observation that might be of help in reducing anxieties encountered in the eight major categories of sexual behavior cited earlier.[1]

---

[1] The material that follows is based on points discussed by Dr. Maurice Levine in "Psychotherapy in Medical Practice," Chapter 9 in *Sex and Marriage*, The Macmillan Company, New York, 1942, pp. 214–18.

1. Minor difficulties in sexual performance on the part of both men and women are normal and to be expected. This is especially true in the first years of marriage when some difficulties are almost universal. Some lack of orgasm in the woman and occasional premature ejaculation or impotence on the part of the man are to be expected. Why is this important? Because so many young married people have been thrown into a turmoil of anxiety by a misinformed person intimating or directly telling them that their problem was of a deep-seated and serious nature, when it may have been merely a matter of adjustment and growth and development in the marital union.

2. Minor variations in the size of the sexual apparatus do not interfere with sexual satisfaction or pleasure, a fact not known by many people and worthwhile bearing in mind.

3. Many different forms of sexuality between marital partners can be regarded as normal and mature. Often people come to physicians deeply disturbed about this problem. As far as we know, most human beings have some so-called sexually deviate impulses and desires. And as far as we know, many people may satisfy such desires in a marital relationship as a preliminary to intercourse without being considered emotionally disturbed or abnormal if such activity is a mutually desired or acceptable form of behavior on the part of both partners. Certainly, it is not a part of a mature marriage if one of the partners forces the other into undesired or otherwise unacceptable activities. There is a second point of view toward this clinical problem that should be mentioned, one that is directly opposed to it but that is the accepted working basis for many clinicians in this area of work. This view holds that any form of sexual behavior not ending with the union of the genitals of the marriage partners constitutes a symptom of a lack of personality maturity and should be treated as such. The first viewpoint is stressed, perhaps, by biologically oriented observers and clinicians. The second attitude belongs more to those who stress the so-called psychological

or emotional factors in the sexual union. Whatever attitude we accept as our own clinical orientation, it would be my hope that we would do so with objectivity and forethought. It is most important that our counterattitudes to the phenomena that we are observing and to the people we are trying to help be as free of prejudice and judgment as is possible, since we are dealing with a subject that is highly charged for most human beings.

4. Another clinical point to remember is that men and women do have periodic fluctuations in sexual desire, with a tendency to follow a certain rhythm. If the clinician is not aware of this fact, he may not handle a particular complaint in reference to mutual desires or lack of desire in an objective and scientific and understanding manner. Another related factor is that hyposexuality or hypersexuality is not necessarily an indication of a higher type of personality, as many patients may try to tell you. On the contrary it may be a sign of emotional conflicts or endocrine variations.

5. Finally, masturbation or past deviate experiences such as transient homosexual contacts do not indicate that a happy marriage is impossible of attainment. Also, the relatively slower sexual responsiveness of women as well as their ability for orgastic release have probably been greatly exaggerated, both percentagewise and as a factor in the production of emotional symptoms or of marital discord, a misapprehension that probably comes from the masculine orientation of much of the literature on the subject.

In summary let me say that it is possible, from the medical and counseling viewpoint, to recommend and develop in people a general attitude of acceptance of sexuality, particularly in marriage, as something worthwhile, decent, productive, healthy, and a source of gratification and solidarity in marriage. This can be accomplished with very few, simple clinical facts if, as counselors, our attitude remains as objective, scientific, warmly accepting, and nonmoralistic as is humanly possible.

Chapter 17

Sexual Adjustment as Seen by the Gynecologist and Obstetrician

PAUL O. KLINGENSMITH, M.D.

W HAT I am about to share with you is not a systematic study of sexual maladjustment but rather some observations about the problem gained from fifteen years of active practice in obstetrics and gynecology. I would remind you that impressions are not scientific facts and that they can be used for little more than guides to thinking. I have not used an arbitrary yardstick against which to measure the sex life of my patients. My point of reference is a relative one. I look on patients as being maladjusted when adequate reassurance does not meet their needs or when they turn up with a major symptom complex as a result of maladjustment. This is not an ideal definition by any means; it admits to the fact that there are many women who are not ideally adjusted sexually but who have compensated well enough not to have a major problem within themselves, or to create one for their husbands.

Some students of the problem of sexual maladjustment would feel that my definition is unsatisfactory for lack of a critical end point. Many psychoanalysts, for example, say that the most mature emotional response of a woman to sexual intercourse consists of the vaginal orgasm. Then a recent textbook on psychosomatic gynecology implies that the majority of women derive little or no pleasure from the sex act. Now, do we believe that lack of vaginal orgasm or of consistent pleasure in sexual intercourse is tantamount to maladjustment? No, that fact only sets the stage, and then the actors play the varying scenes, depending upon their ability to adjust to something that is short of an ideal. I would accept those who have compensated without major difficulties as being sexually adjusted. The story of a patient may help to illustrate my point.

A woman of forty-five arrived in my office requesting an examination. The crux of the interview was that she had been at a bridge luncheon and from conversation with members of the party had come to the conclusion that she had not enjoyed sexual relations through the years as much as others had. Now she was disturbed, even though she had lived through twenty years of a happy marriage and a sex life which she previously thought to be satisfactory. Now, would you say she is maladjusted? No, she is very well adjusted to something less than the ideal described by a bridge partner.

But even from my perspective sexual maladjustment does lead many patients to the office of the gynecologist. Rarely do I get through an afternoon without seeing at least two patients whom I believe to have symptom complexes arising from sexual maladjustment. Almost no one volunteers that she has such a problem. The guises in which the fact comes are as varied as the Parisian fashions, though certainly not so well advertised. However, there are certain complaints and situational problems that alert me to the need for detailed knowledge of the patient's sexual history, which can best be obtained by steering a circumspect course and not crowding the patient.

The most common complaints are dyspareunia, or painful sexual intercourse, altered vulvovaginal sensations, and chronic pelvic pain not necessarily related to coitus. The problem of sterility, absolute or relative, may be closely allied or due to sexual maladjustment. Menstrual and nervous disorders due to presumed pituitary-ovarian imbalance require careful evaluation of the emotional-sexual axis. Then there is a small group of women who present themselves for examination without overt complaint, hoping the physician will lead them to a discussion of a sex problem.

The complaint of painful intercourse is not tantamount to a diagnosis of sexual maladjustment, but it is the most common symptom of it. When a pelvic examination does not show a disease process but instead reveals vaginismus, the diagnosis of a sex problem will almost certainly be confirmed by a well-taken history. Vaginismus is not to be confused with the normal initial tension in the pelvic floor observed in patients coming to a new physician for a gynecologic examination. This type of muscle spasm relaxes with gentle examination and persuasion on the doctor's part. Vaginismus is persistent spasm which defeats his ingenuity to overcome. It is an overt expression of the fear-tension cycle common to sexual maladjustment. The absence of vaginismus in older patients does not weigh against the possibility of a sex problem, since the muscular vaginal sling may have wearied of resistance.

Altered vulvovaginal sensations or pain in the ovarian areas should alert the physician to the possibility of unresolved emotional conflicts. Normal vulvar skin does not itch nor does normal vaginal mucosa burn without reason. Unfortunately, the ovary is not so directly accessible to examination and few doctors appreciate the fact that chronic ovarian pain and tenderness may be due to causes other than local anatomic disease. A typical case history may serve to emphasize the problem of chronic ovarian pain resulting from sexual maladjustment.

The patient presents herself with a history of chronic abdominopelvic pain. She is in her late twenties or early thirties, and the pain dates back to about six months after marriage. Most often it began in the right, lower abdomen and was especially likely to be severe immediately or the day after sexual intercourse. In the next two years "attacks" occurred more frequently; she lost weight and did not get pregnant. After several examinations and blood counts, an "interval" appendectomy was carried out and a "cyst" on the ovary "punctured." During convalescence the pain was gone but it returned as normal duties were resumed. Menstrual irregularities appeared and the diagnosis of endometriosis entertained. Androgens were given until acne, hirsutism, or voice changes ensued. Whatever relief came was only temporary. Finally, in desperation, the right tube and ovary were removed for "cysts," although the ovary actually looked free of disease. Again, she had a happy recovery, but soon the same type of pain occurred in the left ovary. Now, thin and chronically anxious, she may even go on to further ill-advised surgery.

Though the mechanism of this symptom complex has not been demonstrated clearly, it does not occur in sexually well-adjusted women. It is peculiar to women who enter marriage with lack of knowledge or with fear of coitus and to whom the act becomes a chore. The expression of emotional conflict in ovarian tenderness is not easy to understand, but there is some evidence that two possibilities exist. Doctor Howard Taylor, Jr.,[1] has presented a scholarly review of the subject and has forwarded support to his thesis that emotional conflicts may produce chronic ovarian hyperemia with gradual fibrosis leading to the trapping of follicles, stromal stretch, and chronic tenderness. Other authors raise the possibility of an altered hypothalamic influence on pituitary functions with uncompensated discharge of follicle-stimulating hormone resulting in multiple cystic ovaries, stromal stretch, and chronic tenderness. Regardless of the mechanism, the clinician who finds chronic ovarian pain and tenderness should resist the temptation to treat without a well-established diagnosis.

[1] Howard Taylor, Jr., "The Congestion Fibrosis Syndrome," *American Journal of Obstetrics and Gynecology,* vol. 57, p. 637, New York, 1949.

A painstaking exclusion of ovarian disease and a studied analysis of the sexual-emotional content of the patient are indicated. This latter element of the study may reveal the true problem.

An investigation of couples who present themselves for a study of sterility may prove that the problem is really one of sexual maladjustment. This is rarely obvious from the initial interview but may be suspected from one of several findings. At the time of the initial pelvic examination, the presence of a narrow introitus and vaginismus suggests that coitus may not have been consummated. This suspicion may be supported by additional history or the absence of sperm in the vagina after presumed relations. When the male has a good sperm picture on direct examination and maintains erection satisfactorily the problem lies, primarily, with abnormal resistance on the part of the female, usually the result of the sex-fear-spasm cycle.

Sometimes the sterility study reveals male impotence or, in rare cases, failure of ejaculation in spite of good penile erection and vaginal entrance. These defects may have physical causes, but more often they result from deep sexual conflicts. Male impotence may be relative and compounded by insistence on a schedule such as may be set up by an eager physician trying to catch the ovulation time. I recall a fine young man who came to talk with me after some six months' study of him and his wife. Previous findings had shown an excellent sperm picture and a good delivery of sperm to the vagina. His expressed concern was that at probable ovulation time he could not maintain an erection or make entrance, although at other times in the cycle he was effective. This was probably not so much a sexual conflict as a conflict unwittingly introduced into an important sexual matter.

A more subtle and elusive problem in sterility which may be of emotional origin is the appearance of menstrual irregularities with failure of ovulation. Usually there is no overt sexual maladjustment and the patient seems to exhibit endocrine imbalance. Depending upon the resources of the physician, the existence of an endocrine imbalance may or may not be well established. Well-designed treatment plans of substitutional hormonal therapy may fail to correct the defect. In such instances it is provident to consider the need for careful evaluation of the psyche of the patient. Not infrequently, the resolution of an emotional conflict will meet the need of the patient after hormones have failed. Whether this problem can be said to constitute a sexual conflict or be of other emotional origin I defer to someone better versed in psychiatry.

Another source of case finding of sexual maladjustment comes from women referred for a review of the possibility of ovarian dysfunction causing chronic tension symptoms. Invariably these women suffer from excess fatigue, insomnia, headaches that are more severe around the time of the menses, easily disturbed gastrointestinal function, and menstrual abnormalities. Most of them have children, though rarely more than two or three. The disability dates back to the period following the birth of the first child. Examination rarely shows concrete evidence of ovarian dysfunction, and there is little or no vaginismus or other anatomical defect. The histories are complex with many problems difficult to evaluate and one gets the feeling that socioeconomic difficulties may play a major role. Closer scrutiny of the history may bring to light a lifetime of sexual aversion based upon a lack of knowledge and progressively unhappier experiences with sexual contact.

In older women with this symptom complex the menopause is blamed, but some of them have histories going back ten or fifteen years before any physiological failure of ovarian function would be likely, their stories often disclosing a lifetime of sexual displeasure. Another smaller group has a shorter duration of disability due to tension and describes a satisfactory sex life until recent years. Perhaps the husbands are so diverted by business or other self-interests that love goes unrequited. Others whose children have grown and whose husbands continue to exhibit sexual interest become haunted by the fear of pregnancy, which fear is more common in premenopausal women than is generally appreciated. (Of course this fear can readily occur in younger women who have had three or four children at close intervals.) It has been said that women will go through almost anything both to get pregnant and to avoid getting pregnant. Be assured that this is true and that when the stage is so set, symptom complexes will arise from conflict over sexual relations.

Three categories of patients come to the gynecologist who have no specific complaints but "want an examination." In the first group the approach is direct and healthy, a periodic examination as part of a routine health measure being, indeed, the intent. Others come because of cancerphobia or because of advice from another physician which they could not accept. Their problem is not germane to our present discussion. It is to the third category that I would direct your attention. Invariably they are composed, well-dressed, and speak gently. They come, as Alvarez has said so well, to lead a low card in the hope that the physician will be holding a higher one. Only the alert doctor will learn that they have a problem, since their whole social background makes the articulation of sexual conflict difficult. They do not grossly exhibit the conflict and are deeply grateful to the one who can recognize and resolve it.

The recognition of sexual maladjustment and its tremendous potential for disturbing body function is but half the story. What has the gynecologist to offer in treatment or, better still, prevention? The emphasis should be placed on prevention because a fixed pattern of sexual maladjustment is most difficult to resolve satisfactorily. The opportunity for prevention presents itself first when mothers of young women come for examination. Many of the worst fears concerning sex and childbirth have been introduced into the minds of young girls by their mothers. Mothers can at least be made aware of the need to avoid telling of "horrible" experiences and to recognize that their own conflicts need not be perpetuated through subsequent generations. Furthermore, they should be reminded that young girls will get sex information from whatever source is available and that sound indoctrination at an early age will prevent misconceptions. Many mothers are ill-prepared to educate daughters in sex and would be wise to seek the aid of an experienced physician or marriage counselor.

Major sexual conflicts may begin with marriage, and adequate premarital counseling is the single most important means of preventing them. Many young people are so well endowed that they successfully adjust to marriage without difficulty in spite of the lack of adequate knowledge. However, it is unsound to assume that this will be the case. I recall a mistake I made some years ago that will illustrate this point. The daughter of an intelligent up-to-date family came to me a week before her marriage. Both of us were pressed for time, and she had few questions. I assumed from her fine family and excellent education that detailed anatomical indoctrination was unnecessary. She had normal structures with only slight vaginismus and seemed satisfied with the superficial advice given. Fortunately I did emphasize that she return shortly after marriage if there were any difficulties. Thus a potentially distressing situation was averted when, on the return visit, I learned that attempted sexual relations were producing increasing pain and frustration. Examination now revealed intense vaginismus. A more detailed history showed that her knowledge of anatomy was of a textbook sort without integration to herself or her sensations. She did not know how to deal with a fear-tension complex and had found that sexual contact was far from the pleasure she had anticipated.

Adequate premarital counseling requires time and interest on the part of all concerned, and the interview with the bride-to-be should take place sufficiently in advance of the marriage date to permit time in which to correct defects. A preliminary discussion to help relax tension and learn the basic gynecologic history is in order. I prefer to proceed to the pelvic examination with the thought that the findings thus obtained will permit more specific personal advice. Special attention is given to the size and elasticity of the vaginal introitus and to the presence of vaginismus. The patient is oriented during the examination to the sensation of stretch on the hymenal ring and pressure on the pelvic muscular floor. This permits the examiner to gauge the degree of coaching and other measures needed to prepare the patient adequately. Rarely, one encounters a hymen so tight and inelastic that no simple measures of dilatation will suffice, in which case a surgical resection of the inelastic tissue is recommended and carried out, but only with the consent of all concerned. Obviously, this procedure should take place well ahead of the marriage date so that good local healing can occur. In many young women the introitus may be snug but elastic. Some dilatation and self-education in the sensation of stretching are in order. This can be accomplished by coaching the young woman in the use of a lubricated douche nozzle, pyrex tube, or tampon. One of the minor blessings of the tampon era has been the useful dilatation of the vaginal introitus and the helpful self-orientation in local sensation in that area.

When the examiner finds marked vaginismus he should appreciate that a more extensive reeducation in anatomy and emotional outlook is necessary. The mechanism of vaginismus is explained in detail with emphasis on the basic strength of the vaginal tract and the lack of danger of injury. Careful instruction in self-education to sensation is given. It is assumed that the patient already has an abnormal fear of this area, and a personal review of sex attitudes is supplemented by a well-chosen book on sex. The book should be geared to the individual's capacity, and its content should be familiar to the physician (see Appendix).

Another important element of this interview deals with the discussion of the expectations of emotional response to sexual intercourse. Well-adjusted married couples are fully aware that their sexual response may be altered at times by fatigue or family anxieties, but a young couple may expect a fully satisfactory response to coitus in spite of entering marriage in a state of emotional and physical exhaustion from the pre-wedding parties and plans. Also, they may not appreciate the fact that often the emotional response to sexual intercourse in the female is acquired only gradually, after thoughtful love-making, and that it can easily be disturbed when frustrations or feelings of not responding properly come to mind.

The opportunity should be afforded to speak of family planning. The present economic structure is such that many young couples may desire to postpone pregnancy temporarily. When this is the case advice must be geared according to the religious convictions and specific needs of the couple. At the end of the first interview another meeting before marriage should be planned if there is any doubt in the examiner's mind as to the adequacy of the preparation of the patient. An additional discussion with the prospective groom may be very helpful. Finally, it is essential to make clear that a return visit after marriage at any time will be welcome. Many young couples with a real problem are too proud to admit that they are in trouble unless they know of a truly interested and sympathetic adviser.

The treatment of dyspareunia in married women due to vaginismus follows much the same principles noted in the discussion of premarital counseling. It is probable that a distorted sex attitude has become fixed and will require more painstaking reeducation. The possibility of fear of pregnancy must be considered and, if present, dealt with adequately. Also, more than one interview is needed to accomplish a proper interpretation of local sensation. The patient must be made aware that effort, time, patience, and faith are needed. There is no substitute for the exhibition of genuine interest on the part of the examiner.

The management of sexual difficulties related to sterility

may vary widely. Transient male impotence in connection with planned coitus at probable ovulation time responds more to straightforward explanation of the psychological mechanism involved than to insistence on a schedule of sexual intercourse. Persistent male impotence or failure of the ejaculatory mechanism presents a most difficult problem which I find myself—and extroverted urologists as well—unable to solve. I believe it results from a deep sexual conflict which requires expert psychiatric analysis. Expert help may also be required to resolve some of the blocks in the ovulatory mechanism in the female. However, much can be accomplished by learning why the patient is so desperately insistent about pregnancy and educating her away from this cause of anxiety. There are little tricks, too, that are useful such as a relaxing vacation, getting rid of basal temperature charts, introducing a hobby, or even getting the husband to buy his wife an unexpected fur coat.

The treatment of sexual maladjustment in premenopausal women with fixed tension states is extraordinarily difficult. However, it is not hopeless. Sometimes one is pleasantly surprised to see what can be accomplished by interest and understanding. The recognition of the fear of pregnancy and adequate advice may reduce the tension. Correction of the common misconceptions of the meaning of the menopause and the awakening of a new constructive interest may change a frustrated woman into a well-adjusted one. Refractory patients may be led to a productive relationship through marriage counseling.

In summary, the gynecologist sees sexual maladjustment in many facets of practice. Certain symptoms, notably dyspareunia, may direct attention to it, but a high index of suspicion in other symptom complexes leads to its proper recognition. The finding of vaginismus in the absence of local pathology is practically pathognomonic of sexual fear, but the absence of muscular spasm does not exclude the possibility of a sex problem. The exclusion of local pathology and a well-directed history are needed to support a proper diagnosis.

Strong emphasis has been placed on the preventive aspects of sexual maladjustment and the means of accomplishing this end. Established symptom complexes can be corrected or alleviated by genuine interest and discernment and by enlisting the aid of a marriage and family study and service group.

Chapter 18

Three Common Sexual Problems:
Masturbation, Homosexuality,
and Impotence and Frigidity

O. SPURGEON ENGLISH, M.D.

EVERY psychoneurosis is said to have a sexual component in that there may be too much conflict over sexual matters or a too broad deficiency in libidinal interest which prevents a human being from having a sufficiently warm interest in his fellow man. In any case there are certain people whose neurosis consists of a problem directly and specifically related to sexual functioning. In this chapter we are concerned with three common disorders—masturbation, homosexuality, and impotence and frigidity.

MASTURBATION

Masturbation is now regarded by most workers in the field of human behavior as a normal phenomenon in human development. The manipulation of the genital organ, in either male or female, for the purpose of pleasure is a normal urge for gratification that is not essentially harmful emotionally or physically. In fact it is felt that a moderate amount of masturbation is inevitable in the course of psychosexual development in order to direct power-

ful emotional energies into their proper channels and to fix the
potentiality of pleasure in that particular area of the body that
is best suited to discharge it to the benefit of the individual and
society.

Infants and children of all ages will masturbate eventually if,
in their early attempts to do so, they are not shocked or threatened to abstinence early in life. Some degree of masturbation
is present in most young children, with a tendency to increased
frequency between the ages of three and six and twelve to fifteen.
This is due to the fact that between three and six the child's
sexual curiosity is rapidly developing and also to the fact he is
in his first active love relationship with the parents—a love relationship that subsides as he progresses in school and adapts himself to emotional attachments outside the home. At puberty the
onset of activity of the sexual glands gives added impetus to the
sex urge which tends to increase the practice.

Should we imply then that no restraint whatever need be put
upon the child's tendency to play with himself? Yes, with certain
reservations. If the child is inducted into an interesting play and
work life and if the adults in the environment are not too shocked
and emotionally disturbed by the practice when it does occur,
it will take care of itself with the passage of time. Since so many
adults still carry an attitude of taboo about masturbation and
since so much prejudice exists, we usually have to put some
prohibition upon the child. And there is no reason why we cannot put *some* responsibility upon him regarding this activity as
we do about getting dressed, eating in an orderly manner, and
similar conformities. We state the problem this way to make clear
that the practice itself is harmless. If it offends our aesthetic sense
let us change our aesthetic values and let us get away from the
generally accepted but erroneous notion that the masturbating
child will become insane, delinquent, or asocial in some degree.
As to the child who masturbates too openly or too continuously,
we should realize that he is lonely and tense and trying to find a

gratification in his own body that should better come from mothering, more affection, and a wholesome interest in other children and play. One can say to the child: "People may not understand your reason for touching yourself like that. They may disapprove of you and hurt your feelings because they feel it doesn't look nice. Also your playmates may tease you for it."

The attention, affection, play, and discussion of social disapproval should be enough to handle the masturbation if the relationship between the adult and child is good. If the relationship is not good, the effort should be made to make it more friendly and mutually enjoyable.

It is rather useless to get involved in the question of when masturbation is too frequent. Better to ask: Is the child happy? Does he enjoy other children and play? If this is true the masturbation will stay within bounds, for when a child is normally happy, he simply will not put himself too far beyond the bounds of approval.

It is even more important to ask the same questions about the masturbating adolescent and adult. Is he happy, is he sociable, is he guilty about masturbation? Is he so preoccupied with sex as to detract from his work? If not, then he can masturbate once a month or once a day and he will not be harming himself. He will make a good social adjustment and he is likely to solve his sexual tension through marriage when the proper times comes. People vary in the amount of sexual tension they need to discharge.

Some may ask: "If a person accepts his masturbation, will he want to marry when the time comes?" The answer is certainly he will want to marry; and he may even have a better chance of marital happiness than those who have had their sexuality too repressed through the years. Masturbation is a lonely and incomplete expression of sexuality and will never become the *first* choice of healthy people.

So in conclusion let us concern ourselves not with the negative question of *not masturbating* but with the *positive* matter of providing wholesome friendships and play and work opportunities, and the sexual energy will find its eventual proper social outlet.

HOMOSEXUALITY

Homosexuality is a psychoneurotic reaction in which the individual has the urge to find emotional or physical satisfaction, or both, in the company of and in close physical proximity with a person of the same sex. This tendency is not inherited except possibly in a few rare cases of people who possess the organs or parts of organs of both sexes. Homosexuality comes about by a faulty training or education in matters of sex, so that the sexual energy (libido) does not find its way naturally to a person of the opposite sex. When sexual energy is thus misdirected, certain fears or ideas have blocked the flow of psychic impulses in their normal heterosexual channel. The faulty attitudes of parents or other adults who interfere with psychosexual development can appear at any phase of development. A taboo on masturbation placed on the child in infancy, for instance, may impress him with the idea that to feel pleasure within the genital region is wrong. Since there are other areas that give sensual satisfaction, these will be called into play when normal development is blocked: the mouth, anus, skin, or breasts become charged with a potentiality for pleasurable gratification. When this is combined with hostility, fear, disgust, or indifference to the opposite sex, an unfortunate combination of psychological forces leading to homosexual activity results.

What creates this antipathy to the opposite sex? A number of things can cause it such as the parent who makes fun of the little boy's and girl's natural interest in each other's sexual parts, the parent who implies there is something dangerous or immoral in the mixed play of children together, the parent who says or implies that sex between male and female is dirty, disgusting, immoral, degrading, asocial. These parents are so obsessed with inveighing against heterosexuality that it never occurs to them that they cannot so easily block such a strong force as sex and that, by closing the way to heterosexuality through fear and prejudice, they invite an indirect, unsatisfactory, and less approved route to sexual expression through homosexuality.

Other factors that favor homosexual personality formation are the tendency for certain boys to imitate, be like, or otherwise identify themselves with the mother, and certain girls to do likewise with the father. They are prone to do this when the relation with the parent of the opposite sex is blocked by rejection. Also early seductions into homosexual behavior by adults or older or more aggressive children tend to create unfortunate habits or *fixations* when the emotions and ideas surrounding sexuality are in the formative state. It is to be remembered, however, that there are many normal heterosexual people who have had seduction into a homosexual affair but were not too impressed by it or held within its grasp.

Some homosexually orientated people marry and have children, but they usually have difficulty in being happy and in really loving the marital partner and may be drawn to affairs with persons of the same sex or of the opposite sex, either from some degree of desire or from a wish to conform to social norms. They are called bisexual as well as homosexual.

Treatment

Homosexuality being a neurosis is curable like other neuroses. However, it is difficult to cure. Why? Because very few homosexuals want to be cured, a fact poorly understood by some. They may struggle with their homosexuality and be unhappy with their personality difficulty, but they avoid the work of cure. Intensive psychiatric treatment of many months' duration does not always cure these cases. Homosexual love affairs are unsatisfactory and are often burdened eventually with strife because of the childish emotions of at least one of the partners. Being neurotic, homosexuals are prone to be immature, sensitive, jealous, domineering, and emotionally hungry. A certain number make a fair social adjustment and even an excellent social contribution. But too many of them are unhappy, frustrated, ineffectual people who stand as an object lesson to us for the need of a more enlightened, tolerant education in sexuality.

IMPOTENCE AND FRIGIDITY

Impotence and frigidity should be discussed together since they are practically always due to the same causes. Impotence is the inability of the male to achieve an adequate erection of the penis and maintain this erection for a reasonable length of time during sexual intercourse. Frigidity is the inability of the female to have satisfactory genital pleasure sensations during intercourse which would lead to orgasm.

In some cases organic nervous pathology of the brain or spinal cord or local structural change in the sexual organs will predispose a person to these conditions, but in the vast majority of cases the causes are due to faulty psychosexual development, that is, faulty development of the mature emotional orientation of the individual.

The sex organs are the organs of reproduction and important in the execution of the love act. Human beings may caress with the hand or lips or bring their bodies together in a nongenital embrace, but the ultimate expression of mature physical love is the union of the genital organs. For this to take place the organs must be energized with good feeling while thoughts of love or love play are taking place. If, during the course of growth, ideas of physical love-making are allowed to appear, develop, and flourish within the mind, this capacity for pleasant stimulation of the organs will take place naturally. Just as the thought or sight of food brings blood to the stomach, activates digestive juices, and prepares for the act of digestion automatically, so likewise do thoughts, sight, and touch of the desired person set in motion nerve impulses which bring about erection in the male through blood entering the penis and which bring about secretions of fluid and a desire for contact in the female. The healthy male needs and desires to penetrate a cavity—the vagina—and the female derives gratification from receiving the penis within the vagina.

Now, many ideas can be put into the mind running counter to the positive ideas about sex which should ideally promote good sex organ functioning and pleasure. These ideas fall into certain groups as follows:

1. *Fear of Disapproval or Punishment.* If during childhood and development every sex act such as masturbation or interest in the opposite sex or questions about sex has been met with disapproval, scolding, shame, disgust, or threat, then the mind can know only distress in connection with sexual functioning. It is as if a laboratory animal were given a painful electric shock every time it tried to take food, until only pain was connected with food to such a degree he could not eat.

2. *Hostility towards the Partner.* We have said that the sex act is a love act. Now, not all husbands and wives love each other. In fact they may very definitely hate each other. Boys or girls may be so strictly brought up as to feel only hate toward human beings as oppressors, thus entering marriage feeling that no gentleness or consideration can come from another human being, especially one of the opposite sex. A boy who has hated his mother will surely hate his wife in some degree. While some people may be able to have hate in their souls and at the same time have sexual intercourse, others cannot. They need to feel love in their minds (and lots of it) to energize the sexual organs with pleasure. The man whose penis will not become erect or stay so is saying with his body: "I don't want to love that way. It shames me, dis-

gusts me, frightens me and I just can't give anything to the woman which would make her feel good as long as I hate women." The woman says: "Since I hate men I can't feel good about them with my body. The idea of sexual union with them does not give me a happy feeling anywhere." Sometimes a man or woman may feel hostile toward the opposite sex in such a way as to feel that the genital organ is a means of doing harm to the other.

3. *Conflicting Loves.* Men and women may be unable to love with their genital organs because they have never overcome childhood emotional attachments to some member of the family. A woman may still be in love with her father or a man with his mother (usually unconsciously, of course). As a result such a person feels that sexual union with anyone else is foreign and disloyal. Either partner may have a latent amount of homosexuality. This yearning toward the same sex is bound to detract from the ability to love the opposite sex and this saps the emotional energy which should be deflected into heterosexual channels. Finally a person may be just too much in love with himself —too selfish in plain words—to have any feeling for giving another person pleasure. The sex act is an outgoing act of love in which sensual pleasure to the self is important but in which a desire to give pleasure to the other plays a large role. So we see people whose pleasure is derived from personal achievement, the acquisition of possessions, public endeavors for groups of people, but who cannot direct any expression of affection toward an individual in any intimate way.

Treatment

Having seen some of the causes of impotence and frigidity we can understand more clearly what has to be done in the way of treatment. It is first a mental-hygiene problem. We must have sensible education about sex, which would contribute mightily to prevention. There is no need for the strong taboos and the withholding of sex information. We should have confidence in our young people and believe that if their feelings for physical love-making are allowed to develop, they will still control the sex drive in a kind and considerate way. As a nation we act as if sex were such a powerful force that if it were not held in check by fear and shame it would lead to wholesale self-indulgence and disregard for the rights of others. The fact is that the sex impulse, while powerful, can be brought under the wholesome control of the personality. That has been confirmed many, many times. We do not need merely to suppress. Suppression is negative and is what produces the harm. We must educate positively.

In the individual case, physicians and marriage counselors must try to discern where the greatest difficulty in the personality lies. Is it hostility, too much love of self, fixation on some other loved person? Counseling helps the person in question work on his problem, encourages him to accept a new point of view, tries to desensitize him from his old ideas, and teaches him how to be warmer and more giving with his body.

Unfortunately only a small number of cases of impotence or frigidity can be cured by a few interviews. Not more than a small per cent of cases in our experience have changed without a long period of many hours of work on the personality. When loving with the body is not accepted and quite easy after twenty-five to thirty years of living, the human being needs attitudes changed which have been rigidly laid down. Most cases need the help of specialized treatment by a psychiatrist and some need psychoanalysis. This fact alone should again turn our minds to the importance of proper education in sex for the prevention of these serious personality maladjustments, since few people can afford the time and money for a protracted period of psychiatric reeducation. Society should strive to make its citizens sexually healthy from the beginning.

Part Four

The Meaning and Process of Counseling

Chapter 19

Marriage Counseling: A Philosophy and Method [1]

EMILY HARTSHORNE MUDD, Ph.D.

A MONG other excellent definitions of counseling the sim-plicity of Gilbert Wrenn's statement is most satisfying: "Counseling is a personal and dynamic relationship between two people who approach a mutually defined prob-lem with mutual consideration for each other, to the end that the younger or less mature or more troubled of the two is aided to a self-determined resolution of his problem." [2]

There are perhaps two main points to consider in discussing a philosophy and method of counseling: what does the person who comes for help want and need and how can we best help him to attain what he wants and needs? If with the first point we think beyond the one person and his particular need to a consideration of the basic needs of all human beings, we will have a common denominator that will be at least part of any counseling interview. For instance, who among us does not need to be wanted (loved), to be appreciated, to experience variety,

[1] Based on two published articles of Emily H. Mudd: "Counseling, A Philosophy and Method," *The Cyclopedia of Medicine, Surgery, and Special-ties*, F. A. Davis Co., 1945; and "Psychiatry and Marital Problems," *Eugenics Quarterly*, vol. 2, no. 2, June, 1955. Used with permission of the publishers.
[2] C. Gilbert Wrenn, *Guidance in Education Institutions*, 37th Yearbook of the National Society for Study of Education, 1938, p. 121.

to have the chance to achieve, and to have some measure of security? If we can agree that these factors represent universal needs and are therefore part and parcel of a counselor's philosophy about life and people, they become naturally, in our thinking, part of the situation of each person seeking help. A situation becomes a problem to a person only in so far as he feels it to be so. Therefore, "It is that person's interpretation rather than the situation itself that has to be understood and treated." [3]

As to the second point—how to enable the person seeking help attain what he wants and needs—our attention is again led to certain almost universal conditions in our society. All people are lonely—the difference is in degree only. If the fact of loneliness is accepted as part of the counselor's philosophy about life and people, again it becomes naturally part of every interview. It is therefore of paramount importance that the persons seeking help know that we are interested in them and that we care that they are in trouble.

In addition to being lonely, people are also anxious—the degree of anxiety or fearfulness varies with the individual and, of course, with the circumstance. In wartime, for example, anxiety is evident all around us. In all times, peace and war, it is apparent in persons seeking help. If the recognition of anxiety as an inevitable part of living has a place in the counselor's philosophy about life and people, it is then possible to accept anxiety as a natural part of every person's feelings as they present themselves and their particular situations in the counseling interview. The techniques by which we work are comparatively unimportant compared to the interest and caring we show each person. It is this interest and caring that do more than anything else to ease the loneliness, anxiety, and fear and so make possible the beginning of the use of other help. If, through the counselor's attitude, the person feels free during the interview to express

[3] James Plant, *Present Day Problems*, Woman's Press, April, 1944.

his anxiety in manner or word, he may be helped to focus it and then do something about it.

Sometimes anxiety is about the future, in which case the giving of information, the discussion of something not understood, not yet experienced—if done easily and naturally and cheerfully by the counselor—often relieves anxiety, focuses fear, and enables the person to talk things out, consider alternatives, and think of his plans in relation to his goals.

Sometimes anxiety is about the past and the present, and here the chance to talk about himself and his behavior, to express his feelings and desires, whatever they may be, without fear of condemnation or criticism, often will bring relief and help him focus his problem and finally to move—to do something about his situation.

Let us suggest the following as the essentials of counseling:

1. The importance of individualizing the interview—taking the person from where he is and going on from there.

2. The importance of asking the client a few simple questions, the answers to which will indicate his attitudes toward his situation.

3. Acceptance and discussion of these attitudes by the counselor with warmth and interest and perceptivity. In addition it is important to share reliable information for which need is indicated as questions come up naturally during the discussion.

4. Sympathetic recognition by the counselor of the naturalness of the anxiety or fear or resentment or antagonism that is apparent in most clients, no matter what their problem.

5. Recognition and acceptance by the counselor of the fact that sexual feelings and experiences are a normal, natural, and vital part of life and therefore inevitably have a place in adjustment. The type and amount of this experience vary with the individual. Judgments as to the rightness or wrongness of aspects of behavior in this area of living are changing as new scientifically sound information is made available. Often there is a

great deal of guilt and fear about this phase of human relations that are a result of misinformation or misunderstanding rather than a result of the experiences themselves. When indicated by the situation, the counselor, if and only if he feels comfortable in such a discussion, should be ready to discuss attitudes and responsibilities in this area, and so help the client release the fear and guilt and develop more health-giving behavior.

6. Realization by the client that the opportunity to talk out the way he feels about things with a receptive, sympathetic, and realistically oriented counselor is probably more important to him than covering any prescribed amount of information.

7. Reassurance by the counselor that learning to get along with other people in the home, at school, on the job, and so on requires time and patience and almost always involves incidents that are disappointing and unsatisfactory for one or more persons. This does not mean failure, but indicates opportunity for improvement.

8. A basic belief by the counselor in the need for spiritual values and their forcefulness in shaping the destiny of man, no matter what the religious affiliation of the client. This should be inherent in the quality of the relationship between counselor and client whether or not it is discussed verbally.

We assume a philosophy of helping that has grown through the belief in the meaningfulness of one human being to another. We utilize an approach that includes techniques, ideas, and concepts from different methods of helping. This philosophy holds that everyone has a right to available knowledge, that most people, if accepted as they are, without condemnation or manipulation, will respond to naturalness, understanding, and warmth. Through the relief of being themselves, of having information practical to their needs, of feeling that their troubles matter to someone else—that someone cares about them—through understanding something of how people can grow and change, they can then go on to the utilization of the innate strength inherent in some degree in everyone. Through being able to express to an objective person their hostility and fear, to live over again under favorable circumstances some of the experiences that were responsible for the accumulation of negative feeling and so to be relieved of it, a burden passes from the client. A change of attitude is then possible and people "become able to survive and even live creatively within the same framework that existed when they first sought help, or find the courage, initiative and faith to effect a difference in their surroundings by their own efforts." [4]

At this point we might well ask ourselves the direct question: What actually is marriage counseling? Marriage counseling is defined as the process whereby a professionally trained person assists two persons (engaged or marriage partners) to develop abilities in resolving, to some workable degree, the problems that trouble them in their interpersonal relationships as they move into marriage, live with it, or (in a small number of instances) move out of it. The focus of the counselor's approach is the relationship between the two people in the marriage rather than, as in psychiatric therapy, the reorganization of the personality structure of the individual. The theoretical framework behind this approach presents the following hypothesis: if an individual can experience, during the counseling process, new understanding of himself and his marriage partner and more satisfying ways of using himself in his daily relationships in marriage and with his family, he should be able to apply these acquired abilities to other problem situations as these arise in his daily living.

Since marriage involves two persons, it has been our philosophy, as in many other marriage counseling services in the United States, to make every effort to work with both husband and wife.[5] When one partner refuses counseling initially, however,

[4] Emily Hartshorne Mudd, "Marriage Counseling," *Cyclopedia of Medicine, Surgery and Specialties,* F. A. Davis Co., 1944, 450–460.

[5] Emily Hartshorne Mudd, *The Practice of Marriage Counseling,* Association Press, Inc., New York, 1951.

we start with the partner who desires help, and in over 75 per cent of our cases we do have contact with both partners.[6] We experimented with having each partner work with his own individual counselor and scheduling periodic conferences between the two counselors to keep in touch with progress but found the procedure time consuming and expensive as well as often confusing and even separating in effect upon husband and wife. Hence for the last five years or so we have scheduled a single counselor to work with both husband and wife. Each partner is seen separately at weekly interviews of approximately forty-five to fifty minutes each. As part of the intake process and at intervals, when deemed appropriate by the counselor and each partner, a joint interview with husband and wife is held, fantasy and reality often meeting for clients and counselor in this three-way conference.

We realize that there are special problems of transference and countertransference inherent in one counselor working with both husband and wife. Thus it is necessary that the marriage counselor have a very real self-awareness of his dual role, of his identifications, biases, cultural prejudices, religious, moral, ethical, and sexual codes of behavior, as they may affect and be affected by the vagaries and perhaps divergent codes, religious affiliations, and so on of his two clients. He must clarify at the onset the confidential nature of his relationship with each partner so that they can trust his integrity and discuss their feelings, behavior, and biases with freedom and candor, knowing that these confidences will not be discussed with the other partner unless he so desires.

By establishing a continuing relationship with each partner

[6] Figures based on unpublished studies of intake at Marriage Council in 1945 under funds from the National Institute of Health, U.S. Public Health Service, and in 1954–55 made by Hilda M. Goodwin, D. S. W., in *An Inquiry Into the Use of the Tri-Dimensional Relationship in the Process of Marriage Counseling*, Unpublished Doctoral Dissertation, Univ. of Pennsylvania School of Social Work.

the counselor can learn far earlier in the contact than when working with one partner only how much of the material presented by the client represents projection and how much reality. When the stories of events experienced together during the week continue to be unrecognizable to the counselor, for instance, it becomes obvious that one or both may be distorting reality. On the other hand when the counselor receives almost identical descriptions of events from each partner over a period of weeks, even though these partners are at daggers drawn, it is apparent that, no matter how difficult the situation, he is dealing with problems and situations that appear to have the same reality for both persons. By keeping the focus on those factors in attitudes, feeling, and behavior that precipitate disturbance and suffering from one or both spouses, the counselor is able to discuss with each client the early experiences that appear to the client to be the source of his present value system and resulting behavior. Obviously the counselor must recognize the kind of apparently satisfying balance that two individuals, whether "normal" or neurotic, can work out in a marriage. Only if there is dissatisfaction on the part of one or both partners would a couple come for marriage counseling. In such a case emphasis would be on the way the neurotic behavior affects the partner relationship.

Discussion in the area of sexual relations can often be particularly rewarding in terms of understanding certain of the dynamics of the personalities involved and some of the characteristics of their interrelationship. Schedules initiated in our research program to cover information concerning sexual feelings, attitudes, and behavior are utilized during the counseling session at the discretion of the counselor.[7] These permit obtaining systematic material from both husband and wife about something presumably jointly experienced. The discrepancies in these

[7] E. H. Mudd, H. B. Froscher, W. L. Peltz, and M. G. Preston, "Effect on Casework of Obtaining Research Material," *Social Casework*, vol. 31, no. 1, pp. 11–17, January, 1950.

reports and the indicated lack of information in the estimates by one partner as to how the other partner thinks and feels give important clues to the emotional overtones and blocks of each person.[8] For example in a marriage in which both clients recognize a sexual problem based on the husband being desirous of more frequent coitus than the wife, it can be predicted on the basis of our research findings that the husband will be likely to estimate sex relations as occurring on the average of say once weekly, whereas the wife will probably estimate them at three times weekly. The distortion is in the direction of what the individual feels he most resents, the husband exaggerating his deprivation and the wife the amount of his demand. The actual reality is probably somewhere between the two reports.[9]

When the same counselor works with both husband and wife, many such examples of the emotional overtones that color and distort the impressions of reality of an interpersonal relationship are apparent. With skill these discrepancies can be discussed, the emotions involved explored, and, with the reassuring relationship with the counselor who often performs the role of the kindly, caring, permissive parent surrogate, the client can risk modifications in his former behavior. As new experience brings more satisfaction and less frustration, these risks are consolidated—communication between husband and wife is effected on both a feeling and verbal level, and behavior is recognized within a more realistic framework.

In certain cases the counselor suggests that the client supplement the counseling interview by reading material. Sometimes seeing the written word or finding discussion by other thoughtful persons of the subjects under exploration aids the process of

[8] M. G. Preston, W. L. Peltz, E. H. Mudd, and H. B. Froscher, "Impressions of Personality as a Function of Marital Conflict," *Journal of Abnormal and Social Psychology*, vol. 47, no. 2, Supplement, pp. 326–36, April, 1952.
[9] M. G. Preston and E. H. Mudd, "Combining Research and Counseling in the Field of Sexual Behavior." Paper presented at the Groves Conference, Columbus, Ohio, April, 1953.

assimilation of new ideas, information, and the reorientation of attitudes, feelings, and finally behavior.[10]

EVALUATION OF THE RESULTS OF MARRIAGE COUNSELING

It is recognized by thoughtful persons that the psychic attributes of the human organism are being subjected to only the early stages of scientific scrutiny, and the same limitations hold for objective scrutiny of the processes involved in attempting to help troubled persons with problems of personal or family adjustments. The stresses and strains that precipitate physiological or mental pathology naturally vary in different cultures but are inevitable to some degree in all. During marriage counseling, which aims at enabling the upset persons to develop more bearable interpersonal relationships, what actually happens within the inner sanctum of the interviewing room is, with few exceptions, a matter of nebulous obscurity to all but the two participants. There is little scientific information available concerning what effect a series of interviews with an analyst, psychiatrist, clinical psychologist, social worker, or marriage counselor has on the adjustment of a disturbed individual or distorted situation.

In recent years in many countries an appreciable increase in undertaking the assessment of the outcome of such services has been evidenced in most professional disciplines and specialties. It is healthy that a few pioneer scientists have ignited curiosity among the younger practitioners. It is also fortunate that questions are being asked by these newcomers as well as by boards of directors and intelligent laymen which even professionally trained and experienced persons find it hard to answer. A cultish apathy will furnish little eventual protection from the necessity of proving through scientifically acceptable methods that our hypotheses concerning how people are helped can be subjected to verification and proof as to their reliability and validity. An

[10] Listings of books found to be helpful to clients can be found in appendix.

effort in this direction has been undertaken by our Division of Family Study. Under funds from the United States Public Health Service for the last six years we have studied factors affecting marital adjustment and have also attempted to evaluate the results of marriage counseling.

As a beginning our research team published a method of known reliability for recovering information from discursive case records,[11] and subsequently an analysis of a sample of these records was made, including a judgment of the movement of clients during counseling—improvement or lack of improvement, that is, "the extent to which the client has increased in decisiveness, experienced release from tension, and acquired useful information, new techniques, or greater understanding with which he can deal more successfully with his problems, and so on. Types of problems brought to counseling, the counseling techniques used, and the effectiveness of these techniques have been analyzed in part and many of these items have been treated statistically." In a group of cases in which both clients and their partners were counseled we found that approximately "5 per cent of the cases showed retrogression, from 25 to 30 per cent showed no movement (improvement) at all, and from 60 to 66 per cent showed positive movement (or improvement)." In studying the various factors affecting movement in counseling we have concluded as follows:

1. Biographical factors point in the direction which indicates that clients are people rather than statistics. Age, education, and the other bases on which the population is often fractionized seem not to play any essential role in determining movement in counseling.

2. The evidence points strongly in the direction of the fact that the determinants of movement are multiple and complex.

[11] M. G. Preston, E. H. Mudd, W. L. Peltz, and H. B. Froscher, "An Experimental Study of a Method for Abstracting the Contents of Social Case Records," *Journal of Abnormal and Social Psychology*, vol. 4, pp. 628–46, October, 1950.

3. There is some evidence to support the view that the setting of a permissive, encouraging atmosphere and relationship is the principally helpful function of the counselor.

4. There is substantial evidence to support the conclusion that, if both marriage partners come for counseling, husbands and wives counseled separately and independently, although usually by the same counselor, move together; that is, if one improves the other improves and if one retrogresses the other retrogresses.[12]

MENTAL-HEALTH IMPLICATIONS

In the daily adjustments of the marriage relationship, certain people are first conscious of extreme disappointment, anger, and emotional disturbance. Others suffer from physical symptoms, the origin of which cannot be discovered by routine medical examinations. In any case they need help. Because in the last decade in the United States popular articles, books, and radio and television programs have emphasized the subject of marriage and family living, many upset or anxious persons will refer themselves or their friends for marriage counseling. They seek this service from a physician, a minister, priest, or rabbi, a social agency, a psychologist, a teacher. Others with less knowledge or more desperation turn to the law, as Judge Winnet states in his chapter on marriage and the law. The majority of these persons would hesitate at this stage in their problem to resort to psychiatry. Experience has indicated that nine out of ten such couples who have marital problems and who come for counseling can be treated through counseling and that approximately two-thirds of this group can obtain some degree of relief and learn methods of resolving their difficulties. The tenth person can usually be aided to accept referral for psychiatric treatment.

[12] M. G. Preston, et al., "Factors Affecting Movement in Casework," *Social Casework*, vol. 34, no. 3, pp. 103–111, March, 1953, and E. H. Mudd, "Knowns and Unknowns in Marriage Counseling Research," *Marriage and Family Living*, vol. xix, no. 1, Feb. 1957, 75–81.

The extent of marital unhappiness and upheaval, as indicated by Dr. Bossard and others in earlier chapters, creates social, community, and personal disturbances that cannot be ignored. Efforts to deal with these extensive problems involve the training of competent marriage counselors in many professional disciplines [13] as well as the finding of new methods for the development of more adequate individuals.

Adequate marriage counseling facilities, which emphasize knowing what not to undertake as well as what to undertake, offer services supplementing those of psychiatry. Such facilities deal with troubled persons at incipient stages of their difficulties, or when the difficulties, although of long duration, have not resulted in mental illness. Because marriage counseling contacts are brief compared with average psychiatric contacts, the individual cost is substantially less even when psychiatric supervision is maintained. If 66 per cent of counseled cases show improvement, it appears that marriage counseling can offer a service auxiliary to that of psychiatry toward the mental health of the community. As marriage counseling becomes concerned with increasing the facilities for educational experiences of younger persons before marriage that may enable them to develop into more adequate husbands and wives, it should shoulder its responsibilities with greater competence.

SUMMARY

Counseling consists of helping a person come to grips with his problem, take hold of it himself, and do something about it. A philosophy of counseling as discussed herein would agree that the counselor should not be dogmatic, insistent, or too guiding or he may influence the person seeking help to lose initiative, become dependent, or drift into the avoidance of

[13] K. E. Appel, M.D., E. H. Mudd, Ph.D., and P. Q. Roche, M.D., "Medical School Electives on Family Attitudes, Sexual Behavior and Marriage Counseling," *Journal of Psychiatry*, vol. 112, no 1, July, 1955.

responsibility. To help meet the needs of the person seeking help, the counselor will be warm, supporting, tolerant, considerate, accepting, sympathetic, and patient, but not indulgent. Helpfulness will be given by showing interest in the other's concerns and problems and occasionally offering suggestions of possible and alternate plans of action, and above all by letting him feel that we care what happens to him. People do things—change their opinions, attitudes, points of view, and behavior—more because they like the other person and feel that he wants to help and makes efforts to help, rather than just reasoning, making lengthy explanations and appeals to will power and exhortations, or moralizing.

It takes time to change, to grow, to make adjustments, to develop competence. Therefore patience is necessary and not hastiness, sympathy not indulgence, tolerance not criticism, faith not pessimism. People do not want too much fuss made over them; neither do they want to be pitied. They have to feel their way. Many will find themselves through trial and error. The counselor should not argue, blame, criticize, moralize, or tell the other person that he is wrong. He should not humiliate or tell the counselee to be ashamed of his unusual or erratic behavior. He should express approval for real effort to become more adequate, even though success is not immediately forthcoming, and above all, he should show a warm human responsiveness, a sympathy with human differences and an understanding of them, and an awareness of spiritual values.[14-17] The goal of counseling is to help people over the spots that seem rough to them and through this process enable them to help themselves and those with whom they are most closely associated.

[14] Alphonse H. Clemens, Ed., *Marriage Education and Counseling*, The Catholic University of America Press, Washington, D.C., 1951.

[15] Jerome D. Folkman, *The Cup of Life: A Jewish Marriage Manual*, The Jonathan David Company, New York, 1955.

[16] Seward Hiltner, *Pastoral Counseling*, Abington Press, Nashville, Tenn.

[17] Carrol Wise, *Pastoral Counseling, Its Theory and Practice*, Harper & Bros., New York, 1955.

Chapter 20

Three Ways of Relating: Identification, Transference, and Object Relationships

M. ROYDEN C. ASTLEY, M.D.

WHEN a man and wife, troubled about their marriage, seek marriage counseling, they enter a relationship in which there are certain elusive factors. These have to do with the ways in which one person sees or reacts to another.

For years there has been a great deal of discussion about what psychotherapy is, and about whether counseling, social casework, or the work that a clinical psychologist does differs in some essential way from psychotherapy. One thing, at least, is clear: something occurs in the relationship between two individuals, one of whom, the patient or client, is seeking help from the other, a professional person, which makes it possible for the patient or client to undergo a change. The purpose of this chapter is to examine this relationship closely, with particular attention to what the psychotherapist or counselor brings to it.

There are three main ways in which people are able to approach one another or to respond to one another. The first of these may be illustrated by the following incident. During the war, a man was waiting for a train on the platform of a large railroad station in an eastern city. All around him were men whose families had come to see them off. Many of the women and children were crying, and the whole scene was laden with the sadness of wartime partings. The man waiting on the platform, moved by the scene about him, noticed a train announcer who evidently worked day after day in the midst of this outpouring of emotion. He walked over to him and said in a friendly way: "A railroad station must be a hell of a place to work in in wartime!" To his astonishment the announcer replied: "Yeah, these damn soldiers think they own the place!"

This is an example of an attempt to approach a relationship with another person by way of fellow feeling. The man evidently expected, perhaps without thinking about it, that the feeling of the train announcer would be similar to his own, and that they would have a common meeting ground on the basis of sadness and distress. In technical psychological language, such a basis of fellow feeling is known as *identification.* Although it often enough serves as a beginning for people's getting together with one another, it cannot be relied upon, for reasons that are evident from the story quoted above. For one thing, individuals do react differently to different situations; for another, the motives for reaction in any individual vary tremendously according to time and place.

Different kinds of identification can be discerned in people's behavior. The weak person may identify with someone who impresses him as strong in order to bolster his own sense of power, as when a small German villager identifies with the power of a Hitler or when the insecure adolescent takes great pride in being a student at a particular high school or university. Or the strong may identify with the weak, as when a dean goes to a good deal of trouble to help a student in difficulty or when a wealthy person behaves charitably toward an impoverished acquaintance, without regard to whether the student or the acquaintance desires the help. In any case, identification is based preponderantly on subjective factors in the identifier, rather than primarily on careful, objective evaluation of the person identified with. Of course there are exceptions to this rule. The informed and compassionate identification that the mature physician or counselor is able to make after he has become reasonably well acquainted with the other person and his problems is based on thorough knowledge of the situation.

A second way of relating to people may be illustrated by the following situation. A man who was spending several weeks alone in a city far from home noticed that the hostess in the coffee shop in his hotel bore a remarkable resemblance, not only in appearance but also in mannerisms, to his sister. During each meal he had there he was preoccupied with a strange persistent notion that this woman, whom in reality he did not know at all, should be expected to approach him as if she *were* his sister. He found himself unable to avoid the thought that she might greet him affectionately, take special pains to see to his needs, and respond to him with that sort of private sharing of familiarities that grows up between people who for years have been a part of the same family group. In this situation, the man was carrying over from the image of his sister to this stranger, who reminded him of her, feelings that were quite appropriate to the sister with whom he had shared many important experiences. Even though he was well aware of the irrationality of this *transference* (the technical name for this kind of relating), the marked resemblance, plus his loneliness and yearning for a familiar face, resulted in an intense desire to see in the hostess his sister.

It is immediately obvious that if he had permitted a relationship to begin on this basis, the chances of its becoming successful would have been slim indeed: the woman was not his sister, she had not shared his experiences, and she would not have been able to respond successfully on the basis of his fantasy— or in reality, so long as he held to the fantasy.

Identification is the most primitive way in which human beings attempt to establish relationships, and childhood is, of course, the place in which one learns this particular method of functioning. Because it is learned so early, and because it is so useful, it is never entirely given up but continues as part of adult life. It should be added that relationships in which identification plays a large role can be transferred. This can be seen especially in childhood, where, for example, a small boy, intent on attempting, by being like him, to supplant his father in his mother's affections and admiration and approval, may carry his rivalry over into his attitudes toward other larger males who are actually in no sense competing with him for his mother.

Like identification, transference is a process learned in childhood, much used and never completely given up. Both processes are likely to occur without the intervention of reality testing and therefore to impose upon relationships certain anticipations and expectations that are inappropriate. That is to say, these processes are unconsciously motivated. Thus the persons toward whom the counselor relates by transference are being cast in the roles of earlier figures toward whom the counselor had strong feelings in the past, rigidly patterned, which linger within and can be revivified in the present. These feelings partake of the nature of a prejudice or bias, for they represent a failure to take into account the current actuality of the other person.

The third way of relating to people is referred to as *object relationship*. The counselor's relating should be characterized by this mode. Surely it is the relationship toward which he must constantly strive. It may be described somewhat as follows. Other people are consistently and continuously scrutinized and evaluated as objects in themselves. They may, to be sure, remind the counselor of other individuals, but they are not to be confused with others but rather kept individual and separate. There is involved in this scrutiny a kind of ready, on-going curiosity, which, without being too evident as such, nevertheless does help the counselor acquire meaningful and significant data about the other person. As clues come to hand out of this accumulation of data, items from the client's past are utilized so that the counselor begins to form not only a cross-sectional picture of the person as he appears today but also a formulation that makes his present understandable in terms of his past. The wise and mature counselor finds satisfaction, as time goes on, in his increasing capacity to predict the attitudes and behavior of the other person.

At the same time, the complexity of human beings makes it quite impossible for a counselor ever to know another person so well as to know all about him. This fact removes some of the distaste that the more romantic therapists have for such formulations as those just described. What is being urged is not a cold and calculating effort to assay another person as if he were a biological specimen but rather a warm effort to understand him in depth, not only for his own self-interest but for the client's as well. Implied in the effort to create such a relationship with others is a willingness on the counselor's part to permit himself to be known as he really is, with, however, certain qualifications or limitations.

These qualifications can be discussed under headings that describe the approach to another person in object relationships. The first of these is *acceptance*. Acceptance has to do with a general interest in participating in the relationship in such a fashion that the other person can afford to be himself, at least for the time being. Acceptance is illustrated by the attitude good parents have toward a newborn child; the child is received without criticism and is permitted to be what he is, without regard to adult standards of behavior. Naturally, except when professional people concern themselves with the treatment of patients who are extremely ill, such a degree of acceptance is rarely demanded, or even appropriate, among adults. What the example illustrates is the *quality* of the accepting attitude that introduces object relationship.

In step, as it were, with the accepting attitude, there is a second characteristic in object relationship and that is an implication of willingness, even desire, to understand the other person. This *understanding* is not based on idle curiosity, nor is it merely an intellectual exercise designed for purposes of classification or categorization. It may be compared, perhaps, with the desire for mutual understanding which prompts two people who are only slightly familiar with each other's language to attempt to enlarge their capacities for communication by various indicators and signs. It implies a warm and active effort to know the other person by participating with him in what he is.

The third characteristic implicit in object relationship is *steadfastness*, that is, the providing again at least for the time being, of an anchor for the relationship. There should be a willingness to maintain without fickleness the relationship with the other person, not disrupting it except for cause, and for a cause mutually understood, or at least communicated. Steadfastness is the antithesis of what occurs when a man and a woman, with the benefit of alcohol, have become bosom friends, only to find with the dawn that the relationship which the night before was so important has suffered the same fate as the few ounces of alcohol that launched it.

Considerations of reality dictate that the degree of acceptance and its duration must vary with time and place, and with the resources that are brought to a situation. We must of necessity be on guard against putting ourselves at the disposal of anyone who wishes to make claims on us, and also against encouraging people for whom we really have neither time, energy, nor interest. Generally, however, the resources available depend upon one's emotional or psychological state rather more than on reality. Thus one is usually correct in assuming an emotional rather than a factual reason for the behavior of a man who is too busy to be pleasant in his relationships with others. Again, matters of physical health may preclude the acceptance of other people. A man who goes courting a girl who has a severe toothache will not find himself very welcome, because too much of her energy will be taken up with herself for her to be able to turn her interest toward him in an accepting fashion.

Emotional situations, either acute or chronic, strongly affect our ability to be accepting. It is important to note before going further that the acceptance is of the other person as he *is*, and not at all as he fantasies or wishes himself to be. A small child who is playing at being an explorer may be accepted temporarily as an explorer, and if this is honestly done the child will feel gratified because he is truly accepted as a small child playing explorer. But the adult who to offset his sense of inadequacy presents himself as an extremely superior person need not be accepted either as superior or as inferior; he should be accepted as someone who is troubled for unknown reasons and who uses such an attitude in his attempt to get along in the world. The acceptance is of the person, not of his presenting attitudes and behavior.

Understanding also has its limitations. Obviously a person cannot be expected to feel a deep interest in every individual he meets. Our emotional resources are too small for such casual dispersal. Healthy people usually have a small number of other persons to whom they devote relatively large amounts of interest and concern. The most intimate sort of mutual acceptance and understanding is generally accorded members of the family, with the husband or wife as the main recipient. Outside the family circle there will be a few intimate friends, for whom the barriers to depth of relationship will be low and the field of relationship extremely large. Peripheral to the close friends there will likely be individuals and groups of a categorized sort, those with whom one is closely associated in business or in other well-defined common interests, but in other areas only slightly or not at all. After these people, the degree of concentration of interest in relationships will gradually diminish, although the quality of objectivity will be retained, and the capacity for deepening relationships to a greater degree upon an appropriate occasion will always exist.

Out of an understanding of the other person will emerge an evaluation of him which is used for a decision as to the worthwhileness of continuing the relationship. What is considered to be worthwhile will be, of course, a subjective judgment and will vary not only from person to person but also from time to time in the same individual. We do not mean to imply here that an object relationship means intimate friendship. The orientation is usually friendly—but "good fences make good neighbors." There are areas in the lives of all of us that are rightfully opened only to a select few, perhaps to no one. The fact that such areas exist must also be accepted, understood, and respected.

The time may come when it is no longer worthwhile to continue the relationship. We have all had the experience of having been close friends with people whom we no longer value, either because they have failed us or we them; or because we have outgrown them or they us; or because differing experiences, and the differing effects of these experiences, have diminished the possibility of continuing a gratifying relationship. It is pertinent to realize, therefore, that object relationships serve to delimit quite realistically the quantity of satisfaction that one person may derive from another. In addition, if the relationship becomes one of consistent distress or dissatisfaction or boredom, the aspect of steadfastness needs to be changed. Optimally, this change will occur relatively easily, by tacit mutual consent. On the other hand it is generally very painful to us to have to let someone know that we no longer wish to maintain a relationship on the old basis. Great gentleness and tact, as well as forthrightness and strength of purpose, are usually required to diminish a relationship that has for a time been intense.

Even in object relationship, much that we do is below the level of our awareness, somewhat in the way, perhaps, of a mother's understanding of her child—an understanding largely based on her potential for responding appropriately without having actually formulated into conscious ideas the reasons for her response. This is really not very strange. We are, primarily, feeling and operational rather than verbal, and we have, to a greater or lesser degree, a capacity for learning, knowing, and behaving intuitively without conscious thinking. Often one is able to review this process by hindsight and to recognize by thinking the determinants of what has already occurred, a process somewhat akin to the writing of history, which clarifies the reasons for events that have been observed and for which an explanation has been lacking.

On the other hand not all the "thinking" that goes on beneath the surface can be easily subjected to review. Often it can be recognized that we do not know why we have responded as we have, and often reasons that are given seem spurious; they are scarcely plausible and give the impression of having been tailored to fit the situation, instead of the situation having arisen as a result of them. The intensity of a person's belief in such assertions is no measure of their validity, any more than the intensity of a person's love is a measure of the excellence of his beloved, or the intensity of a "not guilty" plea a measure of the degree of culpability. In short, we frequently react or respond first, and then rationalize our attitudes and behavior. In object relationship this way of reacting is held at a minimum.

The counseling relationship, then, which is a special kind, demands sharply defined limits on the counselor's willingness to be known to the client. He permits himself to be known as a counselor, rather than as a social acquaintance. The client's satisfactions, and his own, should derive from the fruitfulness of the work together. Otherwise the same mistakes that the client has made in his past relationships will simply be repeated, *with no new outcome,* in his relationship with the counselor.

Chapter 21

Pitfalls in the Counseling Relationship

M. ROYDEN C. ASTLEY, M.D.

IN THE preceding chapter, we mentioned as criteria for evaluating object-relationships the amount of worthwhileness, satisfaction or gratification that one finds in them. Three agencies of our minds contribute to the extent of these feelings: the essential agency that seeks pleasure, not caring how it may be obtained; the learned agency (a duality, in that it accords praise for meeting standards and imposes sanctions for violating them) that maintains that certain pleasures are good while others are not to be permitted; and the agency that has assumed the task of seeing that the first gets its due without the discomfort of flouting the second or of risking trouble with the world of things and people. The first, the *id*, is like human body structure in that while it varies from infant to infant, it is pretty much the same in all. The second, the *ego-ideal* and the *superego*, since they develop according to individual experience, are more like clothing—something assumed or donned—and show more individual variation. The third, the *ego*, is even more individual, representing all that as separate persons we bring to the tasks of knowing and using ourselves and the world.

The three ways of relating—identification, transference, and object relationship—must therefore always bear an individual stamp. In each case not only will the id be seeking pleasure but the ideals and conscience will insist, on pain of anxiety, that certain criteria and sanctions be taken into account. The ego must find a formula to satisfy these demands as well as those of reality. In addition its task is greatly complicated by the ideals and superego, for though the energy of the superego (how much it can make us hurt) is supplied by ourselves, its content (the rules it insists upon) comes from our reading of the wishes and commands of those who reared us; and, likewise, we strive toward ideals of a similar derivation. Actually the "shoulds" and "should nots" that we live by so much have been taken over from others in an effort to find comfort in conformity. The ego's early task was to deal only with id and external reality, and when the external reality became, as it evaluated it, too uncomfortable (because of fear of being unloved or hurt by the parents), it effected a kind of marriage of the parental code, as it understood it, with itself, making it its own. All of us in the weakness and fearfulness of childhood have chosen security over freedom.

What the child embodies (incorporates) in himself is *his* picture of the parental ideals and prohibitions. Since his judgment is weak and unreliable and since he is prone to exaggerated fears, the incorporated parent figure is inclined to be stricter and more punitive than the parents are. As the years go by the superego is in part modified by the growing ego's increasing capacity to learn. However, almost always there remains a core of the overdemanding conscience of childhood, dictating how we shall be and what we may think and do—and, even more strongly, what we may *not* think and *not* do.

In forming relationships, then, the ego must take the stringencies of the superego into account and accede to them. If the superego demands that the child be strong and self-sufficient to get love, then, despite id wishes to be passive and dependent, the ego is faced with the task of avoiding situations in which the child might feel as if he were being babied. He may not then be able to accept being cared for, even if ill, and may have to rebel against the realistic ministrations of physicians or nurses. On the other hand if the superego demands that the child continue to be weak and incompetent, as if the parents had disapproved of initiative and self-reliance, he will not be comfortable in assuming adult responsibility but will be driven by anxiety and guilt to seek someone to lean on for suggestions, advice, and support.

By the same token if the superego forbids the entertaining of angry thoughts, the child will feel discomfited by the hostile impulses that are part of all of us and become self-condemning at any hint of their presence. If sexual impulses are proscribed, the ego will be at pains to prevent their gratification, or even their having a place in the consciousness. Such considerations, too, will influence relationships. In the first instance they will dictate a withdrawal from the usual give and take of life; in the second they will interfere with a realistic view of the sexual aspects of oneself and the people one meets.

The fact that the superego plays so important a role in personality throws some light on the ego. Originally the attitudes of the superego were ascribed by the ego to the parents or other upbringers, and the ego feared what it saw. It then did what one may often see children do in play: it identified with, made itself like, the strong, feared object and took this new role to heart. A little boy, admiring and fearing the dentist, plays at being the dentist. Once a child of eight, hearing an adult conversation in which the grownups were expressing their concern over a possible Russian attack upon the United States, asked: "If we are afraid they can beat us, why don't we be Russians?" The renunciations that the childhood ego accomplishes as security measures are very complete; but just as oppressed peoples tend to fight back underground, so do the frightening id impulses tend, although repressed by the ego, to gain a way to find satisfaction. Again, this may influence relationships. An unaggressive man may find great pleasure in a prize fight via an unconscious identification with the fighters, and a sexually inhibited woman, while condemning the behavior of a much married actress, may avidly read every word about her, ostensibly to get ammunition for her disapproval but unconsciously out of an identification with her in her sexuality.

In just such a fashion we may use people with whom we have real-life relationships as sources of substitute satisfaction, either for our pleasure-seeking or our condemnatory impulses or, usually, for a combination of the two. It is healthy, for example, for a parent to enjoy a certain amount of vicarious gratification in the excellences and achievements of his child; but if the child is unconsciously expected to serve in large measure to make up for parental lacks, he is being exploited, and trouble ensues. A truck driver who had a strong unconscious desire to be free of ties to home (which, via transference, meant to him a too restricting mother) had a son who was a frequent runaway. The father was consciously angry at the son's behavior and punished him severely, but—unknown to himself—he had subtly painted such an attractive picture of the freedom of the open road and of pride in self-direction that the son was unconsciously impelled to do what his father secretly—and guiltily—longed to do. Even the punishment could be used in such a situation to ensure a repetition of the desired but forbidden behavior.

It is the unconscious wishes and taboos that are patterned in childhood and that cannot be subjected to rational adult thinking that get us into trouble. The truck driver was still to too great an extent, in his unconscious, a rebellious and freedom-seeking small boy. He reacted in his adult home as if this were still his childhood, and via identifications and transferences between himself and his son, this view of life was perpetuated and his childish abortive attempt to resolve his own problem was transmitted for the son to act upon.

PROBLEMS IN RELATING

If those phenomena coming under the headings of identification and transference were always easily discernible to our best adult thinking and easily subjected to our adult judgment, there would be relatively few problems in relationships; but the situation is actually quite otherwise. Our identifications and transferences are generally made without our being aware of their coming into play, and especially without our being aware of their significance for our sense of psychic well-being. They are usually quite unconscious. Thus a person who has not adequately resolved his competitiveness with older men may willy-nilly react without being aware of it—that is, unconsciously—as if authority figures in his adult life were the father figure with whom he contended as a child.

All human beings tend to some extent to react unconsciously in the present as if it were the past and attempt to solve in the present problems that were appropriate to childhood but that were not adequately worked out during the formative years.

The person who is interested in doing psychotherapy or counseling is no exception to this. Ideally, he should have resolved his own childhood problems so completely that the motivations that prompt him in his adult life are no longer colored by the childish aims for which he once strove. On the whole, that is too demanding a goal for any human being. The next best thing is that the therapist be so aware of the pervasiveness of ungratified childhood impulses, or of the ways in which they may be blocked off from gratification, as to be constantly on the lookout to see that such factors do not inappropriately interfere with his adult relationships. It would be appropriate, for example, for a counselor who was very fatigued to seek out a relative or friend who would deal with him happily for a while as if he were a tired child who needed love and care and tenderness; but it would be extremely inappropriate for him to seek the same kind of care from a client. By the same token it would be appropriate for a counselor to set limits on the quantity of verbal vituperation permitted to his child, but inappropriate for him to set limits to what a client might say, as if the client were a child to be reared rather than an adult to be understood.

Thus the feelings and biases of the psychotherapist or counselor must be considered as factors of major importance in the emotional transactions of the psychotherapeutic situation. A brief account of the first hour of a case will serve to illustrate the ways in which these feelings and biases can give rise to problems.

A man visited a counselor complaining that he was having a great deal of trouble in his marriage because of his wife's bad temper and dictatorial ways. She was critical of him in front of his children and friends, claiming he did not pay attention to what she considered important aspects of their life together. For example, she wanted the porch painted. He was a busy man whose time was taken up with serving as committee chairman of the local Cub Pack, with the finance committee of the church, and with teaching Sunday school. He therefore found it difficult to get the porch done. He had spent some time scraping it and had started to work on it during his spare time several months before, but his wife had recently been saying that since he had not finished the job, he was no good. She showed extreme impatience on Sundays, and had actually made a scene in the church because one of his jobs was to remain after church to count the money. The family either had to wait for him or go home alone; they were unreasonably irritable and uncomfortable at having to remain, but did not feel inclined to go on without him. There had been times when, in her anger at him, his wife has smashed china on the floor. On one occasion he had left home, telling her that unless her temper improved he simply could not stay. He came to see the counselor to ask what to do in the circumstances. He assured the counselor that people in the community agreed with him that his wife had a bad temper and that life with her must be extremely difficult.

Although the story given is sketchy, this man's presentation during his first visit was no more than a detailed elaboration of the situation as outlined.

It is immediately obvious that one interviewer might easily identify with the client, who seems to present the picture of an industrious and well-meaning citizen whose good works are not appreciated by a nagging and short-tempered wife. His air of righteous indignation, plus the support he claimed from his friends, might lead the counselor to think of him as someone to be sympathized with and rescued from a bad situation. On the other hand it is just as possible to imagine another interviewer who would respond critically, as if the client were a man who has no time for his familial concerns and responsibilities but leaves these to his wife, while he occupies himself with community activities which serve to make him feel like a big shot. He might then be considered a cold and selfish person, somewhat contemptible in his self-righteousness. In both interpretations the feelings and biases of the counselor would have led him into a premature and prejudiced judgment, precluding a thorough understanding of the situation in the marriage and thus preventing the full use of counseling resources.

The unconscious responses of the client are referred to as the *transference;* the term *countertransference* is used to denote the constellation of feelings that arise in the counselor, in the main unconsciously, as he responds to the client. Inasmuch as the counselor's feelings interfere with his object relationship with the client, they interfere with the work. The countertransference always has an individual stamp, but it is possible to describe several typical and all too frequently encountered constellations of feelings which counselors may bring to their work.

TYPICAL PITFALLS IN THE COUNSELING RELATIONSHIP

The Need to Seek a Feeling of Importance by Rescuing People.
All of us in childhood have felt helpless in the face of powerful
people who seemed to threaten our welfare or existence. The
pain (anxiety) may be so great that these feelings are managed
in part by being relegated to the unconscious—as if one had
closed one's mind's eye to the threat. This process is called
repression. In such circumstances these feelings may continue
without our knowledge to color our view of life. We are drawn
toward persons in trouble, tending to see them as if they were
weak and frightened children who need to be saved from someone or something. We "overidentify" with their "weakness." At
the same time, of course, the possibility of helping someone else
by seeming to save him serves to offset our own feeling of weakness and to bolster our threatened pride. The added fact is, though,
that when a client is dealt with in this fashion—as if he were
a helpless child—his troubles are increased rather than diminished and he becomes either more dependent or more resentful, or both.

The Authoritarian Constellation. Childhood feelings of weakness and inadequacy may lead to overcompensatory tendencies
to inappropriate bluster and show of strength. This sense of inadequacy, persisting unconsciously, may prompt an unrealistic
donning of the role of the authority who knows the answers, with
the result that one becomes a bossy, directing person who requires the acquiescence and subservience of others. Even though
the advice and directions may be good, the strengths and capacities of the client are sacrificed to this authoritarianism, with
disastrous results for the welfare of the client's personality.

Unsatisfied Needs for Love. It often happens that a counselor
is too much motivated by his requirement that the people who
consult him form and hold a good opinion of him so that he
may bask in the warmth of their gratitude and good will. Al-

though it is obvious that one cannot be liked all the time by everyone, this motivation may inappropriately tempt a counselor to a kind of seduction of the client's love. The client finds himself being unrealistically catered to; and sooner or later progress ceases, since the client has no opportunity to behave like a whole human being in the counseling situation, much less to work through any troublesome hostile impulses remaining from his childhood.

Problems of Hostility. The role played by destructive impulses is nowadays recognized as of tremendous significance in relationships between people. The myriad frustrations of childhood —the mere fact of being little may often be maddening—act to stimulate our rage; and then, frequently, we are further frustrated and criticized because we are angry. In such a situation the ego may come to regard anger itself as a terribly bad thing, and this childhood view of anger may be continued into adult life. A counselor caught in this pattern will be so prejudiced or biased that no adequate, direct, mature attitude toward anger in his clients or in himself will be possible. He may unconsciously enjoy in his clients some form of destructiveness that he must deny to himself; or he may act to suppress the client's hostility as he suppresses his own, managing to ward off its expression or otherwise prevent the possibility of its being adequately evaluated either by the client's ego or his own.

So manifold and complex are the hostile components that their proper understanding is a major task of the counselor, particularly in so far as his own hostile motivations and their management are concerned. People fight for love, status, independence, preferment, gratification—indeed, any ungratified id impulse calls forth anger; and this is true also for the counselor. In addition, disparagement, intended or implied, of our standards and ideals is felt as a hurt or threat and tends to mobilize anger; thus the client has, in the hostile aspects of his transference, a ready weapon in criticism of the counselor's competence, understanding, capacity for helping, and so on. If the client has learned something of the counselor's personal life, so much the worse: the unmarried counselor may be badgered for lacking experience or for failure to find a mate; the childless one for lack of experience, impotence, sterility, or not caring; the one with children for stupidity, pride, or for caring more for his own family than for the client. It is necessary that the counselor be sufficiently secure in himself as to be able to scrutinize the hostility he must accept, understand its significance for the client, and be able to discuss it in the most appropriate fashion at the most opportune time.

The counselor's religion, politics, sex, appearance, dress, language, accent, family—nothing about which he may have strong or tender feelings will be immune. Rather, they will attract the client's barbs. Mature and realistic standards, which should be the counselor's in maximum measure, will also inevitably be attacked, partly out of envy and partly because these, too, are thwarting to the id of the client.

Problems of Sexual Drives. The ubiquitousness of the urge to come together or bring together and its salient effect in human relationships are by now an old but not yet well-accepted or understood story. The expression of this urge is the matrix of social life and, in part at least, of nearly all our psychological and physiological reactions. Much loving training, rearing, and ego development are required to bring us to a level of contented and satisfactory capacity for sexual life. The sexual life of the client will always be marred in some way by the childhood patterns that disrupt his life in other ways as well. Difficulty may ensue for the counselor whose own attitudes or practices are still influenced by unresolved problems or whose reality situation is for some reason depriving.

It is evident all around us that sexual gratification is eagerly sought in the mature sense; but it is also evident that people try to make it serve, in various immature forms, as a means of finding comfort, proving competence, or asserting mastery. The counselor must be prepared to meet with equanimity all sorts of sexual material and to maintain, despite his own human tendency to be stirred or affronted, an objective attitude—accepting, understanding, and steadfast. The counselor must always seek to grasp and then communicate the reasons for the client's distress or suffering.

Sometimes the counselor must admit to himself that in a given situation he is, by his own standards, disqualified from working with a client. Thus a Roman Catholic counselor may decide to withdraw from a case in which a client seeks alternatives in regard to birth control and pregnancy which the counselor views as having no place in healthy life. The same might be true in connection with masturbation. By the same token, another counselor may, for personal reasons this time, be unable to retain his objectivity in the face of sexual material. Certainly he should not impose upon the counselor-client relationship such limits or limitations (or lack of them) as his personal prejudices or biases dictate to him as an individual; he should either seek to right his own situation or disqualify himself.

It needs to be everlastingly stressed that none of the constellations listed here ever occurs alone. There will, to be sure, be a predominant pattern, a main trend, but secondary or subsidiary factors must always be present and kept in mind as actual or possible threats of interference in the relationship. For example, as vacation time began to approach, a young woman client began to talk about her counselor's vacation in rather warm terms, expressing her hope that he would have a fine time. Various hints presently suggested that she was alluding not only to his vacation but also to the fact that she would like to take it with him. Being inexperienced as a counselor and shy about this aspect of her transference to him, he missed entirely the anxiety and anger that lay behind her proffered companionability. The client wished, underneath, that he would not leave her at all;

her unconscious dependency led to terror at being left alone, and she was seething with an unrecognized rage at the forth-coming separation. The counselor had to be able to manage his feelings about her sexuality, hostility, and dependency; and of course his own feelings as they came into play could either help or hinder, depending on whether he was in charge of them or not.

Rivalry and Competitiveness. Much that might come under this heading has been alluded to before. Needless to say, the coun-selor who attempts to outdo his clients as he works with them or who considers himself better than they will evoke anger, conscious or unconscious, which must disrupt the work. An-other sort of rivalry, however, should be mentioned. Very often the counselor is faced with a client whose disturbance is such as to fall within the province of medical psychology—of psy-chiatry—and require, for the safety of client and community, that a psychiatrist assume the responsibility for its management. If the counselor is a thoroughly well-trained and experienced per-son, it may be that in reality he is capable of working with the client; if this is the situation, it is to be hoped that upon con-sultation with the psychiatrist a way can be found for him to do so if he and the client so desire. Occasionally, however, a counselor's desire to be of help to such a client is colored also by a wish to "be as good as" a psychiatrist: rivalry and com-petition appear where they have no place and interfere with objectivity and calm judgment. This kind of rivalry and competi-tion with psychiatry appears also against other professionals—psychologists, social workers, clergymen, teachers, not to men-tion colleagues and co-workers.

One of the continuing tasks of the counselor is to divest him-self, within limits of human perfectibility, of his prejudices and biases. This is a difficult task. Indeed, it is much like attempting to take a look at one's blind spots. However, people do learn, and light does dawn. Generally, though, it is not until after a person has had some experience with discussing himself with another, and healthy, person that he is at all consistently able to see and evaluate himself and thus to change. The best way to do this is on a professional level, in talks with and evaluations by teachers and supervisors or sometimes in discussion with colleagues. Or the experience may be of a formal therapeutic sort with a trained and experienced therapist who is able to assess the quality and quantity of work required to meet the counselor's needs, which may involve anything from a few interview hours to a full-scale psychoanalysis. Whatever the source of help may be, the results should be an increased capacity for self-examination and change; an increasing ability to bear with oneself realistically, so that one's biases and prejudices are minimized; and a compassionate objectivity which becomes ever more available as a basis for relationships with one's fellow men and women —which are what clients and patients are.

Chapter 22

Practical Aspects of Marriage Counseling

WILLIAM L. PELTZ, M.D.

I N THE previous chapter Dr. Astley described some of the pitfalls encountered in the personal biases and idiosyncrasies of the individual counselor. This chapter deals with the practical aspects of counseling as they affect the person coming for help. For instance the question frequently arises as to whether people with marital problems should be counseled or whether they should be treated by the family physician, minister, clinical psychologist, social worker, or psychiatrist. Some of the criteria which are helpful in reaching a decision are: is the person who will do the counseling interested in working with and helping people with this type of problem; does he have ample time to devote to the case; has he had special training and experience in the field; and is he a friend or social acquaintance of the couple? Obviously, if he is not interested or if he does not have sufficient time because of other commitments, he can hardly do justice to the needs of the problem. And if he knows the couple personally, it may be more difficult for them to share the intimate details of their married life with him and for him to be objective and unbiased with them. But perhaps most important is the degree of their emotional disburbance or maladjustment. If either partner is seriously disturbed, with severe emotional problems, anxiety, phobias, obsessive-compulsive symptoms, de-

242

pression, or delusions, or if either fails to respond to counseling, it is wise to refer to a psychiatrist.

COUNSELING VERSUS THERAPY

Sometimes questions arise about the similarities and differences between marriage counseling and psychotherapy. Both aim to help people with problems through a personal relationship and both employ many of the same general methods and techniques. Marriage counseling, however, focuses primarily on the marriage, whereas the focus of psychotherapy is on the individual. Even when the focus shifts temporarily during marriage counseling to the personal life, it is with the idea of gaining a better understanding of why the person feels or acts in a particular way in the marriage. Thus in the end the focus shifts back again upon interpersonal relation in the marriage. Such is not the case in psychotherapy. Here attention may be devoted for a while to the marriage or to other relationships or situations, but in the end the focus always comes back to the individual.

Another difference relates to the level of consciousness at which the helping process operates, which in counseling is usually on the conscious level. In psychotherapy, on the other hand, it is apt to be concerned as well with unconscious factors, the childhood neurosis, defense mechanisms, dreams, transference, and countertransference. It may be well in many cases for the marriage counselor to be aware of these things, but they are not his tools of trade, at least to the same extent as they are of the psychiatrist.

Psychotherapy has been described as falling under the following headings: manipulative, suppressive, supportive, educational, relational, and expressive. The final method, expressive therapy, may be on a somewhat superficial level or it may be intensive and deep, as in psychoanalysis. People who do counseling will differ in their viewpoints and methods, but probably most of them will use all of these approaches, with the exception of the last, to varying degrees at different times. And it may well be that it is through the relationship that more help is gained both in counseling and in psychotherapy than through all the other methods combined.

PREMARITAL VERSUS POSTMARITAL COUNSELING

At first glance it might seem that premarital counseling would be easier than postmarital and that no special training would be required for this type of work. Actually, however, the reverse is true. Young people who are contemplating marriage, being younger, are often more flexible and have greater capacity for growth and change; their sensitive feelings require the most delicate type of counseling; often the situations in which problems develop for them involve time limits and important decisions involving parents and others. Hence the most skillful and experienced counselors are needed for premarital cases. (See Chapter 2.)

SHOULD ONE OR BOTH PARTIES BE COUNSELED?

When a marriage problem exists, both partners are involved. Sometimes both come for help and sometimes just one, the other partner sometimes not being aware that help is being sought. The question then arises as to whether the person who comes should tell his partner and whether the partner should be urged to be counseled, too. Sometimes the partner is resistant to the idea of coming.

Whether the person who comes for help does or does not tell his partner and whether or not the partner is willing to enter counseling will reveal something of importance about their relationship, whether they work things out together or separately, how much or how little they confide in each other, and so on. In explaining the counseling process during the first interview, the counselor may point out that both partners are involved in the problem and that therefore it is often helpful if both are involved in the counseling process, that there is a better chance of their solving their problem if one of them tries to change or do something about it in a constructive way than if neither does, and a still better chance if both try to do something about it. If one partner is resistant to the idea of seeking help, it can be pointed out that perhaps as times goes along the situation will change and that the partner will cease to object and even want to participate. If they ask whether they should discuss their counseling with each other (whether one or both are being seen), it should be remembered that one of the chief aims of counseling is to help the couple grow closer to each other. Hence if this purpose can be served by their discussing together the counseling process itself or any aspects of it, this should be endorsed and encouraged.

SHOULD THE SAME COUNSELOR SEE ONE OR BOTH PARTNERS?

When both partners want help, the question arises whether they should see the same counselor or whether each should work with a different counselor. There are often definite advantages to the same counselor seeing both. In the first place if he sees just one, he hears only one side of the problem, whereas if he sees both, he can obtain a more complete and accurate picture. Partly as a result of seeing both sides, he can be more objective and less inclined to take sides with one against the other. There are advantages to the couple as well. Their participating together in the counseling experience may be the first time they have ever tried to solve their problems in a sharing and cooperative way. This may help them not only with the particular problems under consideration but also in their achieving a greater degree of closeness in situations outside of counseling. By verbalizing their feelings and making a sincere effort to resolve their problems, they will have an experience that can carry over into other aspects of their life together. In the follow-up study conducted at the Marriage Council of Philadelphia, a client expressed her experience as follows: "Bringing our problems to the light instead of keeping them hidden and knowing that so many others have the same kinds of problems made us feel we're not alone, and that these just have to be lived with and worked out. Talking them out, I learned to be more direct instead of bringing up a lot of old things."

There are occasional situations, however, in which it is usually better for the partners to see different counselors. The first is when the couple themselves wish it. There is apt to be good reason for their feelings in such an instance and it is usually best to accept the wish and learn the reason later. A second situation is when the partners are not working toward a common goal. One of them, for example, may want to preserve the marriage and the other be indifferent about it, may be having an extramarital affair or actually want a divorce. In such situations it would be extremely difficult for one counselor to work effectively with both partners. A third situation is when a psychiatrist or psychoanalyst is working intensively on a deep level with a patient. To undertake therapy with the partner in this case would increase the resistances in both partners to such an extent that therapy with both would probably fail. It is sometimes indicated, however, either before or during the course of psychotherapy, for both partners to be seen by a marriage counselor in an effort to resolve some of the external reality problems that cannot be resolved by psychotherapy of one partner alone. Or at the time of initial contact it may be indicated for the psychiatrist, himself, to undertake the marriage counseling and then refer one of the partners to a colleague for therapy and he, himself, continue working with the other partner.

JOINT INTERVIEWS

When both partners come together for their first interview and neither has been seen alone previously, the question arises whether to see them together or separately. There can be no hard and fast rule about this, but a procedure that works well in most cases is to ask them whether they would prefer to come into the counselor's office together or separately. Their choice, as well as what they reveal during the interviews, will indicate something about their willingness or capacity to work together. If they are undecided or leave it up to the counselor, it is often found to be helpful to see them together for part of the interview and then separately for at least a few minutes apiece. This gives the counselor an opportunity to observe how they relate to each other when they are together and also to learn if there are certain things that either of them wishes to tell the counselor in private.

They are usually seen separately during subsequent interviews. Occasionally, however, as time goes on, it may be indicated to have one or more joint interviews in order to observe how they relate to each other in such a setting, to clarify certain points on which there is disagreement, or to give them the experience of trying to solve their problems by discussion and cooperation. It may be the first time they have ever discussed certain subjects together, even though each partner may have discussed them separately with the counselor. Here, too, then, there is an opportunity not only for the solution of specific problems but for the development of a closer relationship between the partners as well. Sometimes differences of opinion will be more obvious when they are seen together than when seen alone, and sometimes the attitudes of one or the other partner that lead to difficulties between them will become apparent for the first time. Occasionally, of course, such differences lead to arguments and bitterness with the result that the counselor has to terminate the joint interview.

When one partner has been seen alone one or more times prior to their being seen jointly, it is wise always to see the other partner alone before the joint interview. This is chiefly to lessen the likelihood of the second partner feeling that the counselor and the first partner are in alliance and that he is an outsider. It will tend to bring him into the counseling process through the relationship, however brief, he develops with the counselor. In addition, it is possible that he may offer information or reveal feelings that would not become evident in the joint interview.

EXPLORING THE PROBLEM

The question is sometimes asked as to how to proceed after the person seeking help has stated his problem. Usually, a great deal of information is needed before an evaluation or plan of procedure can be made. The background of the problem in terms of the lives of both partners must be understood. Even when the person seeking help presses for a quick solution, it is well for the counselor to keep in mind that he does not yet know enough about the problem or the partners. Exploring the problem rather than being pushed into premature activity is usually the best role for the counselor. Sometimes the very talking over of the details of the problems may be helpful through the relief of tensions, the person seeing his problem differently, the hopefulness he comes to feel, and the greater degree of closeness to his partner that may ensue. Talking over his problems objectively with an outside person may enable him to discuss them in a more constructive way with his partner.

Asking a few questions, rather than too many, is usually the best policy, and usually those questions that offer an opportunity for the person being counseled to tell about things are better than those that lead him to answer yes or no.

EXPLAINING THE ROLE OF THE COUNSELOR

During an early phase of counseling, perhaps toward the end of the first interview, it is frequently in order for the counselor to explain what his role will be. He might explain, for example, that rather than make decisions and have the people seeking help come to depend upon him, he will try to help them make up their own minds. This may be achieved, he can point out, by his exploring their problems and conflicts with them and by their considering the advantages or disadvantages to various possible solutions. He can point out, too, that even if it takes longer for people to make their own decisions, they are usually better off, more mature, and more satisfied than when someone else makes them for them. It takes time for people to change and therefore the counseling process, too, takes time.

Sometimes patients ask. "Do you think we ought to get married?" or "Do you think we should get divorced?" Exploring the problem and helping people reach their own decisions in these instances, as in others, is usually the best course of action.

Once in a great while, however, it seems perfectly obvious to the counselor that a situation is completely hopeless or that a particular course of action is contraindicated. Even in such cases it is generally unwise to advise or interdict. Perhaps it is indicated at such times to have a consultation with a colleague to see if there is agreement regarding the situation. If there is, then it may be wise to say that in the light of what is known from the published literature or from similar cases, the prognosis is poor. The counselor can point out, however, that it is up to the person to decide which way he will act and that if he decides to proceed in spite of what has been pointed out, the counselor is still eager to help. It should be noted, too, that even when people make decisions that are felt to be unwise or that do not work out satisfactorily and that they even come to regret, they may profit more in the long run by making their own decisions and learning by their own experience and mistakes than they would by having someone else make their decisions for them. They will have gained in independence, knowledge, and maturity by the experience.

AIMS OF COUNSELING

The aims of counseling vary, depending upon the problem and the degree of disturbance. Likewise, in a particular case, there may be both short-range or immediate goals and long-range or ultimate goals. For example, an immediate goal in the early stages of counseling might be to learn about the problem or the marriage, to establish a warm counseling relationship, or to give information, whereas the ultimate goal might be the solution of the problem or an improvement in the marital relationship. Some of the more important aims, then, are to give understanding, encouragement, and hope and to be of help in exploring the issues and solving the conflicts, to give information, make appropriate referrals when indicated, to bring the partners closer together or, occasionally, to help them move toward separation or divorce if that proves to be the only solution, to help them gain greater awareness of themselves and each other and to help them live more happily and adequately.

Even when the counselor cannot see how things will work out or what his ultimate goals will be, it is often desirable that he have some immediate aims in mind and that he let the person seeking help be aware of the fact that there is some structure to what is being done. Sometimes all that the counselor can do after one interview is tell the person he wants to help him and wants to see him again, explain what his role will be, and give him another appointment or series of appointments. Sometimes reading matter will be suggested or, if the counselor is a physician as well, a sedative might be prescribed. These things form at least a temporary plan and can be helpful. It is well to keep in mind that the counselee has probably been groping alone with his problem for a long time and here at last he has talked about it with somebody, has finally started doing something about it, and is going to come back and work on it further. Most important of all, perhaps, he now knows that someone wants to help him. He will go out knowing that something has been planned, somebody cares, and he will have a more hopeful outlook toward his problem and perhaps toward life itself.

THE COUNSELOR'S FEELINGS

The counselor's feelings toward the person seeking help and toward the counseling situation are of the utmost importance. Ideally, the counselor should feel at ease and confident, for if he is tense or insecure, the person seeking help will sense these feelings, consciously or unconsciously, which cannot help but affect the counseling process. It should be added that a sense of confidence and security in counseling, as in other things, will usually increase with experience.

Whereas physicians in medical practice must frequently be aggressive and authoritative when their sick patients are reluctant to cooperate or follow orders, the marriage counselor should ordinarily be permissive and nondirective in his approach.

It is usually better to maintain an objective professional relationship. A social relationship between counselor and counselee involves a dual role for both and confuses issues and goals, often making a helpful therapeutic relationship impossible. It is not necessary, however, to be cold and aloof. Human warmth and interest are important in the helping process, and it is possible for the counselor to be natural and friendly without bringing his personal life into the relationship. Sometimes, however, the counselee asks questions about the counselor's personal life such as whether he is married or has children. This may reflect his wanting reassurance that the counselor will be able to understand his particular problems and it may be right and proper to answer the questions honestly and directly. (This is in contrast to psychoanalytic therapy, where the analyst might decline to answer and be more concerned with analyzing deeper reasons as to why the patient asked the question and what the question reveals about his feelings toward the analyst.)

When a person seeking help is obviously having difficulty in talking and relating during his first interviews it may prove helpful for the counselor to identify with him and show his understanding by saying he knows it must be difficult turning for help or talking about these personal things perhaps for the first time.

THE QUESTION OF CONFIDENTIALITY

If one partner is being counseled it is unwise for the counselor to communicate with the other unless the one being counseled approves. Otherwise when the latter finds out about it, as he usually will eventually, he will mistrust the counselor. It is not necessary that the counselor tell everything he knows or is thinking at a particular time because such information may be more helpful later or may never have to be stated because of new insights that the person, himself, gains. What the counselor does and says, however, should be completely honest. Sometimes the partner or a friend or relative will call on the counselor and ask that the counselee not be told of the visit. The answer to that is that it is wiser for the counselor to say he must be free to decide whether he will or will not tell, depending upon the counselee's best interests. If a relative, friend, or even professional person asks the counselor for information about the counselee, in no instance except that of acute incapacitating illness should it be given without his permission.

It is well known that when doctors get together they talk shop. Perhaps they, like others in the helping professions, are overly prone to discuss with one another the people they are treating or counseling. It is probably needless to point out that the matters that people with marriage problems discuss with their counselors are of the most private and confidential nature and that indiscretion on the part of the counselor in this respect could do great and irremediable harm. The strictest discretion and confidence are of importance.

NOTE-TAKING AND RECORDING

Some counselors take detailed notes during an interview while others, feeling that note-taking interferes with listening or rapport, take none at all but write up the interview from memory afterward. It is impossible to say that one method is right and the other wrong. If the counselor is sincerely interested in the person he is helping and attentive not only to what he is saying but how he is feeling and reacting, there is probably no disadvantage to taking notes during the interview. If the person questions it or objects, however, the counselor should explain his need to remember, and if objection continues he should desist. It should be remembered that note-taking stirs up paranoid feelings in occasional patients and recording devices even more so. Such people worry about the possible existence of such devices even when not actually present. Awareness of and respect for such feelings are important.

It is important, too, that the counselor give his undivided attention to the person seeking help—not doodle, for instance, or be looking out the window or have the telephone ring. By paying attention, the counselor indicates his interest. Also, he should convey the feeling that he has lots of time to devote—even if he has only a little. For example, when the time for the interview is limited, he can say: "Now we have about twenty minutes, so take your time and tell me about your problem. We may not finish this time but can arrange to meet again." Thus the counselor is giving as much time as he is able, and the counselee is put at ease. It has been aptly said that *wanting* to understand people is often just as important as *actually* understanding them. This has been called "appreciative listening."

HANDLING SILENCES

Some people who are seeking help speak easily and comfortably, whereas others are self-conscious and speak with great difficulty. Silences may occur in such instances which may be extremely upsetting to the person seeking help and difficult for the counselor to cope with. It is possible to become comfortable in connection with silences, and at times they can even be meaningful and useful. Sometimes, for example, the person seeking help is thinking and collecting his thoughts, and if the counselor interrupts him and comments or asks a question, he stops the flow of thought or shuts off something that might have been significant and helpful. If, however, a silence becomes too prolonged and is serving no useful purpose, it may be wise to interrupt it. In doing so, one possibility would be to repeat or rephrase the person's last few words or sentence as a statement or question. This might stimulate the continuation of the trend of thought without introducing new ideas.

There is rarely, if ever, a place in marriage counseling for the counselor to be humorous or make jokes. Sometimes a well-intentioned counselor will feel called upon to tell an amusing story or anecdote, believing that this will ease the tension and put the counselee at ease. Actually, however, it may do the opposite, for behind humor there lie significant psychodynamic implications to which the person seeking help may react, even if he does not understand them. Moreover a person with conflicts over delicate and intimate problems may be offended by the counselor beginning his professional relationship in a trivial, supposedly humorous way. Needless to say, it is not being suggested that it is necessary for the counselor to be stuffy or overly dignified. He should be natural and sensitive to each person's needs and responses and try to react appropriately.

Even when the counselor feels that people who are coming for help are behaving in an unreasonable way in the marriage situation or persist in believing things that are untrue or unreasonable, there is nothing to be gained by getting into an argument with them. Their actions or beliefs are usually on a deeply emotional basis. Just as religious beliefs, feelings of national pride, obsessions, and delusions cannot be modified by logical discussions or arguments, so, too, intense feelings or ideas about one's marriage or partner cannot be altered by reason and cold logic. Help to these people comes, rather, through the new experience they will have during counseling, largely through the sharing and growth they will experience in the counseling relationship which they will then carry over into their marriage relationship.

USE OF BOOKS, PAMPHLETS, AND OTHER FACTUAL INFORMATION

People who have problems in relation to marriage, whether before or after they are married, can often derive help from reading in conjunction with their counseling. Hence counselors should be familiar with appropriate books and pamphlets which they can recommend to the people they are seeing. The specific information to be derived from appropriate reading may be extremely helpful in many cases, especially in the area of sexual adjustment.

Perhaps more important than the information gained, however, is the couple's sharing of the experience of reading together in an effort to solve their problems, whether before or after marriage. This may lead to their discussing things with each other which they had previously discussed with no one. Feeling barriers and inhibitions may be diminished and a greater degree of togetherness ensue. (See Appendix.)

Frequently people with marriage problems are in great need of factual information, for instance about sexual adjustment and child spacing, which the counselor should supply, making use of drawings, illustrations, or plastic models along with his explanations. He should be able to discuss and answer questions about male and female anatomy and physiology, various aspects of normal and abnormal sexual adjustment during childhood, adolescence, and maturity, detailed techniques of intercourse and contraception, and problems in relation to children in the family.

Sometimes the question arises as to whether certain things are "right" or "wrong." The counselor's own ideas on this should not interfere with what is actually best for the person seeking help. He should not try to impose his personal moral standards upon the person seeking help, either in terms of excessive freedom from codes or of interdictions. Frequently, however, people can be helped to realize that things they formerly considered to be wrong are actually part of normal, healthy sexual adjustment and so can be more uninhibited and happy in their marital relationship. Here again, in helping them come to see these things, reference to the literature can be helpful.

THE LIMITS OF MARRIAGE COUNSELING

It should be pointed out that the counselor is bound to be disappointed if he feels that he has to solve all the problems of all the people who come to him. Perhaps it is enough that he can help some of them some of the time, and perhaps more than someone without any special medical, psychiatric, or counseling experience. Just as the physician will not succeed in all his cases of heart disease or hypertension, for example, so the counselor will not solve all the marriage problems he works with. Happy marriages do not just happen. They require working at. Each partner has to work at it and take care of it, considering what will make the other person happy, what will maintain and improve their relationship—perhaps a kind word, a gift, a thoughtful telephone call, a compliment, or a considerate knock on the bathroom door. Happy marriages need acceptance, forgiveness, humility, appreciation, willingness to admit one is wrong and to go not just 50 per cent of the way but 150 per cent, over and over again if necessary. Sometimes in marriage counseling something of all this can be conveyed during the counseling process, once in a while by direct suggestion and education or by suggested reading, but more often by indirection and implication —perhaps mostly through the acceptance and understanding in the counseling relationship itself, through the patience, working together, and sharing over a period of time and the growth that comes through learning to make one's own decisions and solve one's conflicts. This is marriage counseling at its best.

Chapter 23

A Reluctant Counselee: A Specimen Case

ARON KRICH, Ed.D.

THE following is a consideration of movement within a counseling situation marked by the contrasting content of the first and final (twelfth) interviews, with each of the partners in a deteriorated marriage held together by the bonds of an underlying sadomasochistic interaction. Special emphasis is placed on the task of holding and relating to a reluctant counselee.[1] Subtle mutations in behavior and response, delicately shaded changes in perception of self and mate, and shifts in role identification are detailed in a case record of many closely packed pages. Numerous factors originating in but extending far beyond the counseling relationship had intervened in the three-month period of contact with the couple to effect dramatic changes which are recognized as being more extreme than in most marriage counseling situations. Schematic selection of incident lacks, of course, the conviction of life. However, an inside view of the counseling as highlighted by the polarity of its beginning and end may be heuristic.

[1] The material presented here is based substantially on a case presentation made originally before a joint meeting of in-service graduate trainees in marriage counseling of the Menninger Foundation and the Philadelphia Marriage Council, March 11, 1955, held at the Division of Family Study, Department of Psychiatry, School of Medicine, University of Pennsylvania.

All material presented here is drawn from case recording done immediately after the interviews and has not been edited retrospectively except where indicated parenthetically. All quoted material is verbatim. Naturally, the identity of the clients has been disguised.

The X's came from an industrial community in a bordering state. Parents of three teen-age children, they had been living under an uneasy reconciliation effected under pressure of a court appearance a year previously when Mr. X had left the home. Mrs. X, a college graduate employed as a dental technician, was a large woman. Vivacious and energetic, she gave at one and the same time an impression of competence and helplessness. Birdlike, she seemed more ready for flight than fight. Mr. X, with only a high-school education—in itself a sore spot in the relationship—was employed as a machinist. He was tall and thin but phlegmatic. An exaggerated politeness and affability shifting to stubborn withdrawal were his hallmarks. The youngest child of a large family, he described himself as "an affectionate person." Mrs. X, on the other hand, felt she had had little affection in her life. She was an only child whose father had died shortly after she was born.

When first seen, Mrs. X described her situation as "desperate." She expressed concern about her husband's mental condition manifested by a "change of personality" from meek compliance to hostile impulsivity. She expressed fears that her husband was a surreptitious alcoholic. On the whole, her picture of the husband —and this was given as the cause of the current difficulties— was that he was "no longer himself." For his part Mr. X gave substantial indication of "complete submergence" to the wife's unabashed domination, alienation from his children, and the recurring pattern of "being hailed before a tribunal" whenever he offered a protest. He spoke of himself as the victim of his wife's "neurosis."

FIRST INTERVIEW

Mrs. X

Mrs. X came in briskly, began to speak immediately, and continued almost without pause for the entire interview. She began by saying "My situation is desperate." It was a long trip from her home, but since marriage counseling was not available in her own town, no sacrifice was too great. Things were so bad at home it was not "fair" to her children. She herself could no longer live under conditions as they were. Without any prompting from Counselor, she went on to say that her husband's "personality has changed." Asked how he had changed she said that from a gentle, considerate man he had become irate, unpredictable, and "completely self-centered." He "resents" his children and speaks of them with "venom." Her husband, Mrs. X declared, had always been known in his family as "the quiet one." Now he had turned into "the belligerent one." With an almost diagnostic air, as though quoting from a textbook, she pointed out that the things that made her husband angry were not in proportion to the extent of his anger.

Counselor said we should try to talk about herself. In the same cooperative, detached manner, reflecting a reading familiarity with counseling procedure, she brightly asked if she should begin to talk about her childhood. Counselor replied there was time enough to go back into childhood; now he would like a little more clarification on what was the immediate cause for coming to counseling. She proceeded to tell how, three years before, she had had her husband in Municipal Court on the occasion of his leaving home. She had been in need of a vacation and had had an opportunity to go to a resort with friends. Although the husband had not objected, when she returned from the trip she discovered he had left home, ascribing his reason for leaving to something she had written in a postcard she had sent home. Her version of what she had written was simply that "it was pleasant to breathe clean, fresh air." Perhaps, Mrs. X speculated, her husband had found in these words something he could distort into a personal affront. (*In his interview with Mr. X immediately following, Counselor got Mr X's version of the postcard incident. It is being introduced here, out of context, to highlight the discrepancy in the subjective experience of the same event by the two people involved. Mr. X referred to the postcard as an old grievance. His attention was not drawn to it by Counselor. To begin with, Mr. X complained, the postcard had been addressed to "The X Kids." He, the head of the family, had been left out. He had resented, indeed felt to be a betrayal and attack upon him, that Mrs. X had written "It is good to get away from all the ugliness and tension."*) Mr. X had been out of the home for a month, staying with his mother and defying Mrs. X's efforts at reconciliation. The couple were brought together, Mrs. X said, by a worker of the Court.

Throughout this first interview Mrs. X was intent on presenting herself as the rational, controlled marriage partner victimized by an inexplicable personality change in her spouse. At several points Counselor tried to get her to speak of herself and her feelings about her "desperate situation." But the focus was so exclusively on the husband and the motivation so limited to enlisting Counselor as an ally in manipulating the spouse that concentration on herself seemed extraneous. Counselor finally took the position that he would simply listen to Mrs. X until the need for self-justification was either exhausted or mitigated by the safety of the accepting relationship he would offer.

Mrs. X had said in so many veiled ways that her husband might be suffering from some mental illness that Counselor asked her to tell him openly just what her fears were. She related that two years before, her husband had been struck by a car. The blow had not seemed severe; Mr. X had required no medical attention. However, shortly thereafter she had begun to notice "strange behavior" in her husband. The changed behavior seemed to amount to the fact that Mr. X fluctuated between meekness and explosive anger.

Along these lines, Mrs. X spoke at some length about her husband's drinking. Even with some exploration on Counselor's part, it was not clear whether Mr. X drank heavily, regularly, or occasionally. She could point to only a few isolated times when she had actually seen him drunk, and these were usually in connection with a party occasion; once, he had actually passed out at home. Here, again, as in the projection that Mr. X was mentally ill, Mrs. X could only externalize around an unspecific alcoholism, the reason for the deterioration of the marital relationship. She could no longer "understand" her husband. They had once had such a "good relationship." He had had "a very good mind." She used to come to him for his opinion. In turn, he used to admire her "quickness" and had nicknamed her "Swifty." Now, all this had changed to resentment and quarreling. In addition, she was concerned about the conflict between children and husband. Presenting herself as the husband's champion in this area, she deplored his distorted view that the children did not "respect" him.

Mrs. X raised some question about whether her husband would appear for his appointment, mentioning that she had left a note for him to come. (*Mrs. X was not aware that her husband was waiting in the reception room. At the end of the interview, Counselor escorted her to the door. She did not immediately go to the reception room but went into the lavatory. Counselor went down to the reception room to meet Mr. X, noting this circumstance because it meant that Mr. X came into his first session without seeing his wife. It subsequently developed that he had planned, even at the last moment, to "make up" with his wife and to urge her to free him from counseling by duress.*)

Mr. X

In the reception room Counselor was greeted by Mr. X with smiling, effusive politeness, insisting that Counselor precede him up the stairs. Once in the office, Mr. X expressed his great bewilderment and unhappiness at being there, saying he was not used "to this sort of thing." At the same time, he pointed out that he was "always being hailed and heralded into court or some lawyer's office" by his wife. His home, he complained, which should be "a man's fortifice" (*sic*), was where he felt the least security. *She*, who should be his greatest support in life, was the one person who constantly dragged his name down. Also, he was not a "loquacious" person. It was his wife, the one with the education, who did all the talking, who could "build up a case" and even put words in his mouth.

Counselor explained that this was not a situation to which one could be "hailed and heralded" and that Counselor did not stand in the position of judge or arbiter. But Mr. X's feelings about being "hailed" into counseling were soon explained by his pointing out that the note his wife had left for him read: "If you don't appear, pack your things and get out."

Counselor wondered what Mr. X saw as the immediate reason

for the marital difficulty. He responded that "even a worm turns." It had been the pattern in his married life that whenever he could not take it anymore and answered back he was hailed into court or given a letter to appear at some lawyer's office. This had happened four times in recent years and here he is again! (*It should be noted that Mrs. X never mentioned the other incidents.*) Later in the interview, Mr. X documented his claims by going to his coat and bringing out a batch of threatening letters and notes from his wife. Mr. X was apologetic about keeping these letters, saying he really should burn them, because he was ashamed of them. (*Among these papers was the postcard mentioned in the interview with Mrs. X.*) In explaining his feelings around the postcard, Mr. X told of numerous instances when he had been shut off from the rest of the family, pointing out that he never got to go on vacation with the rest of the family, being treated like an outsider.

As Mr. X gained momentum in speaking of his grievances, he seemed to forget momentarily that he was present under duress. He went on to say that he was a friendly person. He "likes to embrace and forget," and that is how he had always "made up" with his wife. Then things would go along pretty well for a couple of years until he again got the feeling that he was being completely "submerged." Then he would "answer back" with some of the same words his wife used against him and find himself in court or otherwise threatened. Mr. X came to a moment of self-awareness or at least self-observation at this point, commenting that he found himself talking more here than he ever did. At the same time he felt that he would probably be ashamed to face Counselor again after telling him, a stranger, so many private things about himself. Counselor agreed that it was hard to unburden oneself to someone one hardly knew; but perhaps the knowledge that Counselor was someone "different" would make it easier. With ingratiating respectfulness, Mr. X observed that he understood that my work was "scientific."

Mr. X expressed what seemed to be an important piece of insight in saying there was a "neurotic" pattern here—and he used the word neurotic himself—in which his wife was constantly tearing him down while being oblivious to the fact that she was behaving in neurotic fashion. He pointed out that although his wife had built up a tremendous case against him by hammering away at the fact that he was "frustrated" in his childhood, it could be just the other way around. Quite often, he said, his wife would show him passages in books she was reading in connection with one of her courses and say: "See, this is what it says here about people like you." Mr. X's view of his childhood was unsophisticatedly opposed to this. He was the youngest of six children, born in "the old days" of child rearing, and his father did whatever he could for the family. Mr. X harbored no feelings of resentment. In fact he had a very close relationship with his mother to this day. Indeed, he had arranged to have lunch every day with her! In contrast, he pointed out, his wife's mother had not been "mentally normal." This was well known "to everybody," since she had often made violent scenes and sometimes had run out into the streets at night.

Mr. X was speaking freely and movingly during the last part of the hour. Again and again he returned to the theme of "submergence." He made much of the fact that the family finances were controlled by the wife and that he was on an "allowance" so meager he had to budget it. He never had a penny in his pocket. Indeed if there was a charge for this evening's counseling he would be extremely embarrassed because he did not have the money to pay for it. Though he had a responsible job on which he had worked for ten years—and where the men "look up" to him—his wife dragged him down by saying "any little punk could earn more than you do." Counselor told him that the fee would be worked out and would be dependent on whether the couple continued their counseling.

Although Mr. X spoke about his great reluctance and the pain of having to go anywhere to solve these "private problems," he seemed, by the end of the interview, to be comfortable enough with Counselor to consider a continuing relationship. Counselor stressed his interest in Mr. X for himself, underlined his identity as counselor rather than judge or "policeman" for Mrs. X, and left the matter of continuing up to him. It was Counselor's strong feeling that the one thing Mr. X needed before he could even consider alternatives to his way of relating to his wife was a warm, supportive relationship—in simple terms a friend.

For Mrs. X the first half of the counseling relationship—six interviews—appears to have been devoted primarily to permitting her to air her grievances. Her preoccupation was almost exclusively with the husband's behavior. These were essentially acts of impulsivity selected to show the "irrational, infantile, immature" side of the husband which would give credence to the client's conviction that there had been a "personality change." (One such act had been to fling a book at his teen-age son.) In general, the tenor of the wife's dilemma was that "the quiet one" had become transformed to "the belligerent one." The counselor's occasional attempts to direct the client's attention to consideration of her own behavior were usually overlooked. There appeared to be little or no recognition that what she was saying —with tremendous volubility—was that a man who had been easily, even willingly, dominated was now resisting because he had been beaten down as low as he could go.

The counselor's decision to allow this "self-centeredness" (an accusation, incidentally, made by her against the husband) to go relatively unchecked was based on a hunch that most of the feelings and acts ascribed to the husband were unrecognized projections. The counselor's "active" listening was repaid by the fourth interview when the client spoke openly about "death wishes" against the husband. Up to now she had been expressing her fear of his "violent" feelings. It was in this session too, that the client first raised the question "What can I do?" marking the first shift of the burden of responsibility from the husband to herself. Significantly, it was at the end of this interview that she inquired whether the counselor thought *she and her husband* needed psychiatric attention. However, it was not until the seventh interview that the impact of the counselor's gradually introduced series of connections began to be felt. The case record notes: "The most significant aspect of this session in C's estimation was the failure of the client to mention any complaint against her husband." This progress toward self-examination was verbalized by the client in admitting: "I guess I have been pretty arrogant."

With Mr. X, the counselor's main effort in the first six interviews was to eradicate the atmosphere of coercion surrounding his forced appearance at the agency, while at the same time offering him ways to make some restitution of his destroyed self-esteem. This task was made more difficult by the fact that the client was not unaware that the depth of his debasement at the hands of his wife was so extreme that it might be more painful to speak of it than to continue to live with it. (Mrs. X, for example, had once publicly thrown his pay envelope in his face, and he had had to get down on his hands and knees in the street to recover the scattered money.) At the end of the first interview Mr. X had "embraced" his wife, accepted all the blame for the immediate friction, and was prepared to return to a *modus vivendi* described by him as "serving, serving, serving," until he would be able to "take it" no longer. Then he would strike back and again be threatened with being "kicked out" of his home. He had pleaded with his wife—as he would with the counselor for the next five interviews—to be released from counseling. However, as the counselor continued to emphasize his interest in Mr. X for himself and to hold out for consideration realistic alternatives to complete submission, his resistance gradually changed to ambivalence, and by the seventh session, counseling began to be accepted with involvement and self-interest.

For Mr. X these earlier interviews were given over for the most part to outpourings of self-pity. At the same time his demeanor, particularly at the opening of each session, was tinged with hostility which invited—provocatively—a return of hostility from the counselor. Throughout this phase, the counselor had to be alert against being drawn into the orbit of the client's *injustice collecting*—to use Dr. Edmund Bergler's apt phrase. His manner seemed to say: "Here I am, worthless, humbled, humiliated. Do with me what you will. You, too, will probably humiliate and humble me some more." (My quotation.) However, this self-abnegation had its aggressive overtones. Once responded to, these provocations would offer the injustice which would validate the client's need for masochistic atonement. However, by the sixth interview, he was able to direct his aggression toward concrete situations in the marriage. Thus focused, he was able to set the limits of his own dependency. For the first time, he spoke with vehemence and some strength about certain circumstances under which he had formerly permitted himself to be victimized. Proudly he announced to the counselor: "I'm not *that* docile!"

By this time (sixth to seventh interviews) much benefit was being reflected from actual changes in the home life of the clients due to a more active consideration of the husband's feeling by the wife and a more conscious—as opposed to "explosive"—assertion of his manliness by the husband. It was apparent that Mr. X now felt the counselor to be an ally. In this connection it is interesting to note that this feeling of allegiance seems to have been shared equally by the wife, though with her it was more in the nature of having someone to lean on as she dropped certain rigidities of behavior and attitudes which were characteristic of her defense against deep-seated fears of losing hold of herself. In this manner the remaining interviews were able to be devoted to examining daily experiences in relinquishing control on the wife's part and a corresponding taking over of new responsibilities on the husband's. Most marked was the restored affection and physical intimacy accompanied by the revival of pet names unheard in the home since the first years of marriage. (Symbolic, perhaps, was the fact that Mrs. X whose father, it will be recalled, had died shortly after she was born began often to call him Father.) Incidentally, it should be noted that under continued exploration from time to time, Mr. X's drinking began to be revealed as an occasional act of defiance to his wife's "Hitlerlike" prohibition, and that now Mr. X was offered the opportunity to drink openly in the home. The extent of his indulgence appears to have been one drink before dinner!

Three months later at the final (thirteenth) interview both partners were singing praises of the "miracle" of counseling. The husband summed up his changed status by expressing his feeling that he was now "an entity in the home." The wife marveled at her new-found ability to appreciate the meaning of her own behavior and reveled in the novel awareness that reducing her aggressive pressure on the husband resulted in more positive behavior on his part. A vicious circle of attack and retaliation had been broken. Affection had returned to the home; Mr. X was being taken into the family circle and given a place in the lives of his children; sexual relations which had previously been withheld by the wife for periods as long as a year had been restored, and a nostalgic recapturing of past mutual interests had given the relationship a new quality described by both partners as "exciting, thrilling, wonderful, overwhelming," and so on. Counseling, instituted by ultimatum from the wife and reluctantly endured by the husband, was terminated at her initiative after a period of reality testing in which the husband was permitted to participate as an equal partner. Most significant was the wife's admission, in the final interview, that her original belief that the husband was mentally ill was actually a reflection of her own disturbed emotional situation at the time. (I have chosen the twelfth interview to reproduce here because in reality it marked the termination of the active phase of counseling. For after a two-week interval in which the couple wanted to "try their wings," as Mrs. X put it, they returned for a final meeting which was more than anything else a farewell to counseling.)

TWELFTH INTERVIEW

Mrs. X

Mrs. X was a few minutes late. She apologized, explaining that the snow had delayed her. Unlike her urgent manner in earlier interviews, she did not seem to have the need to talk, appearing reflective but at ease. She commented that she had purchased a dress during her lunch hour. Counselor asked if this had been done to pick up her spirits. She laughed and said, no, she had no need for a pickup; things had been going along very nicely. She was quiet again. It was apparent that the barrage of complaints and self-justification with which formerly she had filled her hour was now alien to her, but not so far in the past that her present manner failed to have something of a secret shared with Counselor. We were approaching a natural ending to the counseling relationship.

Counselor asked if there were some "loose ends" we might tie together. She said there was nothing special she wanted to explore but went on to comment on a pamphlet dealing with marriage which she had obtained. She had been doing a great deal of thinking about some of the things she had read. Prompted by Counselor to elaborate, she declared she had gotten some new slants on the role of a wife. She could see she had made many mistakes. She ended up by asking: "Why do people get married?" The question, like most of what she was saying about herself, was put in a subdued, almost philosophical tone. It was obvious that she did not expect—or need—an answer from Counselor. Her manner indicated the unspoken words: "I have learned a great deal about myself and my marriage."

Mrs. X went on to say that she had been discussing with her husband the question of how long the counseling should continue. (*This question of termination had been raised by Mrs. X a number of times in earlier sessions, but always from the point of view of having an answer to give her husband. Until now her response to him had been either a hostile "Do you think you are ready?" or an authoritative "Counselor will decide!" For the first time she seemed able to consider that the life the couple share together rather than Counselor's omnipotence should be the guide in this matter. Because Mr. X had been coerced into counseling, the manner of termination was both a measure of the couple's progress and an important element in the future of their relationship.*) Mrs. X now said she realized this was a decision that should be arrived at mutually and that she and her husband had spoken about it along these lines. Since it was still early in the interview, Counselor bided his time both to remain uncommitted on the question and to give Mrs. X the feeling that our relationship was still "open."

Mrs. X paused and then brought out that the one area on which she was still puzzled was the problem of her husband's drinking. (*This matter had received considerable airing during the eleventh interview, a week earlier. During a trip she had discovered a bottle of whiskey in her husband's suitcase. There had been an "incident" and Mr. X had accused her of "spying." Incidentally, this was the first time that he himself had ever mentioned the question of drinking. It was pretty clear that his "drinking" had been greatly exaggerated. Mrs. X knew, for example, that her husband had been given a bottle of liquor as a holiday gift. Her shocked discovery amused Mr. X; but he resented her prying.*) Mrs. X invited Counselor to share his impression of the situation. Counselor told her he felt that her husband was not a drinker in the usual sense of the word, that her husband felt that her notion that he drank furtively arose from the fact that liquor was never used socially in the household. She agreed that throughout the period of counseling there has been no problem with drinking. She herself offered the hunch that much of her husband's need to drink might have grown out of the marital conflict. However, she still revealed an underlying concern around the subjective link between his drinking and his "aggression."

With all this, Mrs. X stressed again that they had now found a way of talking things over with each other. They had taken up the habit of going for walks, a thing they used to do during their courtship and the earliest years of marriage; she was very pleased at the revival of this pattern. Counselor observed that it is not the particular device used by a couple to achieve closeness but the emotional climate that makes such symbolic gestures meaningful.

Mrs X went on to speak feelingly of how bad the marital tension had been for the children. At this point her expressions of gratitude were pegged to the secondary benefits from counseling to the whole family. Gradually and tentatively she began to speak on her own behalf. She spoke of the fact that when she had first come, things had looked so black she actually had had very little hope of achieving anything. She looked upon what had been achieved as "almost a miracle." Counselor made no comment, accepting the praise as a compliment to them and the work they had put into counseling as well as to himself as part of the experience.

While Mrs. X was focused on the process of self-exploration, Counselor took the opportunity to recall that in the early interviews she had felt that her husband—and later she—might be in need of psychiatric treatment. He wondered what her feeling was about this now. She agreed that she had been so concerned and "disturbed" at that time that she felt that there was "something wrong" with both her husband and herself. She had suspected that the difficulties—since she saw them as being in and originating with Mr. X—were so deep that psychiatric attention rather than marriage counseling would be needed. She saw now that this was not the case; the whole picture had changed. She recognized that there were still many basic differences between her husband and herself in terms of values, habits, temperament, and goals. She admitted she was still troubled by his "pessimism" and insecurity about "what he is getting out of life." The tone of her acceptance of these "facts of life" and the way she seemed able to integrate them with her own contributions to the relationship seemed to indicate a readiness for a mutual handling of life problems. In essence, then, Mrs. X felt quite confident that the situation had so changed that the thought of psychiatric help for herself—or her husband—seemed quite alien. Counselor pointed out some of the uses and benefits of psychiatry and related it to the experience she had had in counseling. He also shared with her the feeling that she must have been quite frightened and concerned to have been thinking secretly that "something was wrong" with herself while openly being concerned that her husband had suffered a "personality change." Mrs. X handled this with her characteristic self-description: "I guess I was pretty arrogant." At the same time she saw that her husband was much more "pliable" than she had realized. Counselor shared the knowledge that Mr. X has been making the same kind of observation about her, whereupon she revealed that he had already told her so.

The hour was now almost over. Counselor pointed out that it was obvious that the couple had reached the stage where they were examining their relationship independently of him. He invited Mrs. X to speak openly about her feeling about terminating the counseling, saying that clients sometimes feel they will hurt the counselor's feelings if they raise the question directly. It was apparent that Mrs. X welcomed this opening. She agreed that she and her husband had been discussing the matter but felt she did not want to break off either abruptly or totally. She was not sure whether she "knows how to swim" without some support. We discussed various possibilities for tapering off the counseling, finally deciding that they would be seen again in two weeks and at that time we would either terminate or further tapering off could be planned.

The session closed with a rather warm glow of achievement which is difficult to convey. In general the quality of her expressions was one of responsible gratitude to the agency and the process it embodied.

Mr. X

Counselor opened the interview with an explanation of the plan for termination that had been discussed with Mrs. X and asked how he felt about it. Mr. X was all smiles. The symbolic shift of the final decision to continue counseling to *him* was not lost on him. He revealed that he had anticipated this development. He spoke of the fact that several days before, Mrs. X had suggested they take a walk. He felt, then, that he knew what she wanted to talk about. During the walk Mrs. X had told him how much she had gained from the counseling and had asked him did he not feel, too, that they were ready for termination. Mr. X declared that he had been extremely surprised to hear his wife say that *she* had gained so much. This was something the like of which he had not heard for years. Mrs. X was not one to "make admissions about herself."

He went on to relate that his wife had given him the pamphlet mentioned in the interview above. Immediately he noticed that certain parts were underlined. Recalling the many times she had thrust passages from books at him with the comment "This is you!" his first reaction was to want to give the pamphlet back to her. This time Mrs. X noticed his reaction and quickly pointed out that the underlining had been automatic on her part and that actually there was nothing derogatory intended. She backed this up by getting an eraser and removing the markings. This pleased Mr. X tremendously. He read the pamphlet and was impressed by the information it contained.

Mr. X spent the major part of his hour speaking of the many positive things that had occurred in the marriage. For example, he pointed out that in recent evenings while relaxing at home, his wife had walked up to him and kissed him, something that had not happened since the first years of their marriage. He felt that there were many "little things" that had changed—her way of asking him to do things, the fact that she was now calling him pet names, her consideration in seeing that he was not late to work (Mr. X drove his wife to work each morning, which had been a daily source of tension), and finally the renewal of sexual activity on a mutually satisfying basis.

Counselor took this opportunity to review the issue around Mr. X's drinking habits by pointing out that Mrs. X still seemed to have some concern about this. He explained that he drank "no more than anybody else," that actually he did not care to drink. However, he pointed out, he had on occasion taken more than he had wanted out of a sense of revolt, at a wedding, for instance, or on other public occasions when friends would offer a drink and the wife would immediately warn: "Be careful! You know what it does to you, and so on." Then he would drink simply to show his "manhood." His wife's chiding, which he described as "Hitler or tyrant behavior," aggravated him. "She forgets herself and treats me like a kindergarten child."

While Mr. X reiterated some of the bad aspects of his wife's impatient domineering which had made it difficult for him to keep any vestige of dignity, he spent little time in justifying himself, however. His old complaint of "begging for forgiveness until my pants are worn out at the knees" was not heard. And he shared his wife's amazement about what had been happening. As he put it: "I am overwhelmed by the response I am getting from her." Only the Sunday before, he had taken a drink in her presence—the bottle now being kept openly in the kitchen—and she had very politely asked whether he still wanted the tumbler for another. This had "flabbergasted" him.

Counselor worked out the same arrangements for "tapering off" the counseling with Mr. X as he had with the spouse, being careful, even now, to leave the decision up to him. He agreed to the arrangement readily, but in the spirit of a "full partner." He examined "the pros and cons" with relish. To the end, he continued to express great admiration for counseling and what it had achieved. Naturally, he saw most clearly the "effect" on his wife which he found almost "impossible to believe." Counselor stressed that there would be ups and downs; but the main thing was that the two had experienced ways of bridging the gap that arose between them in times of tension. Like his wife, Mr. X. said several times that if he could continue to have what he had right now, he would be satisfied.

In view of what has been reported above, it was Counselor's impression that barring unforeseen circumstances which would nullify the couple's recent experience with each other, the session scheduled for two weeks hence would prove to be the last for this case.

It is the counselor's belief that the interpersonal equilibrium, achieved in part through his support of the dependent and masochistically oriented husband simultaneous with his efforts to reduce the punitive controlling of the compulsive and aggressive wife, is only tentative. At best, it represents a return to the *status quo ante* of the period of courtship in which the husband saw the wife as someone "strong" on whom he could lean, while the wife saw him as "good, kind," undemanding, and perhaps unmasculine. The fact that she, fatherless from birth and lacking a male image against whom she could establish and test her femininity, values highest the soft (as opposed to virile) qualities in her husband, must be weighed against her few expressions of tremendous fear of assertive behavior on his part. A month-long hysterical loss of voice when her husband had once literally shaken her physically is indicative of this reaction. At the same time Mrs. X was quick to call her husband "a punk" and to constantly pressure him for failure to achieve the financial and culturally approved signs of being a man. A postpartum depression following the birth of her first child is also in keeping with the client's diffuse concept of her own femininity.

Mrs. X reveals a family background disadvantaged from the

point of view of preparation for marriage. There is some evidence that her mother was emotionally unstable and possibly given in later years to psychotic episodes. When one considers Mr. X's peripheral position in his original family—he was the youngest and seemingly the most deprived child of an "irresponsible" father and a mother who appears to have taken over the patriarchal role—his readiness to give much to get little becomes understandable. To be punished is also a form of relatedness.

From the material highlighted above, the conclusion cannot be avoided that intensive therapeutic exploration of the character structure of both partners could profitably be undertaken. The traits of masochism in Mr. X and of sadism in Mrs. X have a common and coupled root in the striving to escape from what Erich Fromm has called the "unbearable feeling of aloneness and powerlessness." However, the restored balance in this couple's interaction is not without certain new elements. Their ability to employ conscious motivations derived from counseling to arrive at a basis for living together in friendship must not be minimized. The depth or durability of the adjustment achieved by them cannot be gauged with instruments presently available. I do know, on the basis of inquiry, that "things [were] going well" five months after the last hour of counseling.

Appendix A

Books and Pamphlets on Marriage and Family Living Useful to Husbands and Wives, Parents and Children, and Their Counselors

American Catholic Family, The. John L. Thomas, S.J. Prentice-Hall, Inc., N.Y., 1956.

Art of Loving, The. Erich Fromm. Harper and Bros., N.Y., 1956.

Baby and Child Care. Benjamin Spock, M.D. Pocket Books Inc., N.Y., 1946.

Casebook of Marriage Counseling. American Association of Marriage Counselors. Association Press (in press, 1957).

Discovering Ourselves. Edward A. Strecker, M.D., and Kenneth E. Appel, M.D. Macmillan Co., N.Y., 1952.

Education for Marriage. James A. Peterson. Charles Scribners Sons, N.Y., 1956.

Emotional Maturity, Development and Dynamics of Personality. Leon J. Saul, M.D. J. B. Lippincott Co., Philadelphia, 1947.

Emotional Problems of Living. O. Spurgeon English, M.D., and Gerald H. J. Pearson. W. W. Norton & Co., N.Y., 1945.

The Family, A Dynamic Interpretation. Reuben Hill and Willard Waller. The Dryden Press, N.Y., 1951.

Fathers Are Parents, Too. O. Spurgeon English, M.D., and Constance J. Foster. G. P. Putnam's Sons, N.Y., 1951.

Happy Family, The. John Levy, M.D., and Ruth Munroe, M.D. Alfred A. Knopf, N.Y., 1938.

Help Your Husband Stay Alive! Hannah Lees. Appleton Century Croft Inc., N.Y., 1957.

How to Make the Most of Wife. Margery Wilson. J. B. Lippincott, Philadelphia, 1947.

Interviewing. Annette Garrett. Family Service Association of America, N.Y., 142.

Love and Marriage. F. Alexander Magoun. Harper and Bros., N.Y., 1948.

Male and Female. Margaret Mead. Wm. Morrow & Co., 1949.

Marriage Manual. Hannah Stone, M.D., and Abraham Stone, M.D. Simon & Schuster, N.Y., revised, 1952.

Marriage and The Law. Harriet F. Pilpel and Theodore Zavin. Rinehart & Co. Inc., N.Y., 1952.

The Mature Woman: Her Richest Years. Anna Kleegman Daniels, M.D. Prentice-Hall, Inc., N.Y., 1953.

Menopause. Lena Levine, M.D., and Baka Doherty. Random House Inc., N.Y. 1952.

Modern Marriage and Family Living. Edited by Morris Fishbein, M.D., and Ruby Jo Reeves Kennedy, Ph.D. Oxford University Press, N.Y., 1957.

One Marriage—Two Faiths. James H. S. Bossard and Eleanor S. Boll. The Ronald Press Co., N.Y., 1957.

Practice of Marriage Counseling. Emily H. Mudd. Association Press, N.Y., 1951.

Premarital Consultation, The. Abraham Stone and Lena Levine. Grune & Stratton, N.Y., 1956.

Psychiatric Interview, The. Harry Stack Sullivan, M.D. W. W. Norton & Co. Inc., N.Y., 1954.

Readings in Marriage Counseling. Clark E. Vincent. Thomas Y. Crowell, N.Y., 1957.

Sex Attitudes in the Home. Ralph G. Eckert. Association Press, N.Y., 1956.

Sexual Harmony in Marriage. Oliver M. Butterfield, Ph.D. Emerson Books, Inc., N.Y., 1955.

When You Marry. Evelyn M. Duvall and Reuben Hill. Association Press, N.Y., 1953.

Your Marriage. Norman L. Hines and Donald L. Taylor. Rinehart & Co., Inc., N.Y., 1955.

Public Affairs Pamphlets of Special Interest for Marriage and Family Life

(Available from Public Affairs Pamphlets, 22 East 38th Street, New York 16, N.Y., for $.25 each or at quantity rates.)

Alcoholism—A Sickness that can be Beaten. Alton L. Blakslee.

Broken Homes. George Thorman.

Coming of Age: Problems of Teen-Agers. Paul H. Landis.

Democracy Begins in the Home. Ernest Osborne.

How to be a Good Mother-in-law and Grandmother. Edith G. Neisser.

How to Discipline Children. Dorothy Baruch.

How to Tell Your Child about Sex. James L. Hynes Jr.

How to Teach Your Child about Work. Ernest Osborne.

If I Marry Outside my Religion. Algernon D. Black.

Keeping Up with Teen-Agers. Evelyn M. Duvall.

Live Long and Like It. C. Ward Crampton, M.D.

Making the Grade as Dad. Edith G. Neisser.

Mental Health is a Family Affair. Pratt and Neher.

New Medicines for the Mind—Their Meaning and Promise. Gilbert Cant.

Planning Your Family. Herbert Yahraes.

Saving Your Marriage. Evelyn and Sylvanus Duvall.

So You Think It's Love. Ralph G. Eckert.

Stepmothers Can Be Nice! Helen S. Burgess.

The Modern Mother's Dilemma. Sidonie M. Gruenberg and Hilda S. Krech.

Too Young to Marry? Lester A. Kirkendall.

Understanding Your Menopause. Stella B. Applebaum and Nadine R. Kavinoky.

When Mental Illness Strikes Your Family. Kathleen C. Doyle.

When You Grow Older. George Lawton and Maxwell S. Stewart.

Why Some Women Stay Single. Elizabeth Ogg.

Working Wives and Mothers. Stella G. Applebaum.

Appendix B

National organizations through which referral may be made for service in marriage and family counseling from local sources.

AMERICAN ASSOCIATION OF MARRIAGE COUNSELORS, INC.
104 East 40th Street
New York 16, New York

Robert A. Harper, Ph.D., Secretary

PURPOSE: To establish and to maintain professional standards in marriage counseling. This purpose shall be furthered by meetings, clinical sessions, publications, and research in this field. Membership, established in 1942, is open only to those who meet the detailed requirements for clinicians in the field, to affiliates whose work in this or related fields is well known, and to associates whose background, training, and beginning practice is sufficiently advanced to enable them to gain professionally by meeting with the more experienced counselors. Information concerning membership requirements, qualified counselors, and counseling services may be secured from the Association's headquarters office.

AMERICAN EUGENICS SOCIETY, INC.
230 Park Avenue
New York 17, New York

Frederick Osborn, Secretary

PURPOSE: To promote research on the interaction of biological and social factors in human development and on conditions influencing the distribution of births.

AMERICAN MEDICAL ASSOCIATION
Bureau of Health Education
535 North Dearborn Street
Chicago 10, Illinois

W. W. Bauer, M.D., Director

PURPOSE: To make available general material on health education, including literature on premarital, marital, and family attitudes.

AMERICAN SOCIAL HYGIENE ASSOCIATION
1790 Broadway
New York 19, New York

Conrad Van Hyning, Executive Director

PURPOSE: To work for healthy communities, free from venereal disease and its consequences, free of prostitution and related vice. To promote strong family life, sustained by a healthy community environment, and to protect the health and morale of the Armed Forces.

COUNCIL OF JEWISH FEDERATIONS AND WELFARE FUNDS, INC.
729 Seventh Avenue
New York 19, New York

Philip Bernstein, Executive Director

PURPOSE: The Social Planning Department assists local Jewish welfare federations and their family service, child care, and psychiatric agencies in planning community programs and services. Staff consultation is available to agencies.

FAMILY SERVICE ASSOCIATION OF AMERICA
215 Fourth Avenue
New York 3, New York

Clark W. Blackburn, General Director

PURPOSE: This is a voluntary membership federation, established in 1911, of 267 mostly Community Chest supported family service agencies in the United States, Canada, and Hawaii. These agencies provide professional services in their communities for people with personal and family difficulties, and work to strengthen family life generally. The association helps its members through the sharing of experience, improves standards of service, and develops programs by its publications, field service, institutes, research, public relations materials, etc.

NATIONAL ASSOCIATION FOR MENTAL HEALTH, INC.
10 Columbus Circle
New York 19, New York

Richard P. Swigart, Executive Director

PURPOSE: To develop a co-ordinated citizens voluntary movement to work for the improved care and treatment of the mentally ill and handicapped; for improved methods and services in research, prevention, detection, diagnosis, and treatment of mental illnesses and handicaps; and for the promotion of mental health.

NATIONAL CATHOLIC WELFARE CONFERENCE
FAMILY LIFE BUREAU
1312 Massachusetts Avenue, N.W.
Washington 5, D.C.

Rt. Rev. Monsignor Irving A. DeBlanc, Executive Director

PURPOSE: A family life "secretariat" for the Catholic Bishops and Dioceses of the United States, this Bureau co-ordinates and unifies Catholic family life programs; guides diocesan and regional family directors; helps program for the National Councils (Federations) of Catholic Men, Women, and Youth; presents Catholic family ideas in appropriate forms; arouses public interest; provides a clearing house for information; promotes and produces popular timely literature for all family life levels; organizes specialists in the field; represents the mind of the Bishops in family theory, family education, family organization, and family policy.

NATIONAL COUNCIL OF CHURCHES OF CHRIST IN THE U.S.A.
DEPARTMENT OF FAMILY LIFE OF THE COMMISSION ON GENERAL CHRISTIAN EDUCATION
257 Fourth Avenue
New York 10, New York

A. L. Roberts, General Director

PURPOSE: To continue and extend the plans and programs in the field of family life of the agencies uniting in the Council, cultivating an awareness in all Departments.

NATIONAL COUNCIL ON FAMILY RELATIONS
1219 University Avenue, S.E.
Minneapolis 14, Minnesota

Mrs. Ruth H. Jewson, Administrative Secretary

PURPOSE: To provide opportunities for organized groups, agencies, members of allied professions, and individuals interested in family life to plan and act together voluntarily for the advancement of marriage and family life by means of consultation, conference, and co-operation on the goals, needs, and problems of marriage and family living.

NATIONAL LUTHERAN COUNCIL
Division of Welfare
50 Madison Avenue
New York 10, N.Y.

Rev. Henry J. Whiting, LL.D., Executive Secretary

PURPOSE: To serve as a consultative agency for local Lutheran welfare agencies, to co-ordinate the work of these agencies by state and area, and to serve as a liaison for Lutheran welfare with public and private national agencies.

AUGUSTANA LUTHERAN CHURCH
BOARD OF SOCIAL MISSIONS
2445 Park Avenue
Minneapolis 4, Minnesota

Morton V. Bjorkquist, Secretary

PURPOSE: The Seven Works of Mercy—to care for the sick, befriend the stranger and homeless, minister to the imprisoned, clothe and feed the poor, comfort the aged, protect the children, and counsel the troubled.

PLANNED PARENTHOOD FEDERATION OF AMERICA, INC.
501 Madison Avenue
New York 22, N.Y.

William Vogt, National Director

PURPOSE: To provide leadership for universal acceptance of family planning as an essential element of responsible parenthood, stable family life, and social harmony, through education, provision of necessary services, and promotion of research in the field of human reproduction.

MARGARET SANGER RESEARCH BUREAU (Affiliated with Planned Parenthood Fed.)
17 West 16th Street
New York 11, New York

Abraham Stone, M.D., Director

PURPOSE: To serve as a clinical, teaching, and research center in the fields of human fertility and marital problems.

Index

Acceptance, in personal relationship, 224, 226
Adolescence, premarital adjustments and, 165–167
Adultery, 85, 161
Allen, Frederick H., 65–74, 75
Anal sensation, 38, 77
Anglican Church, attitude toward marriage problems, 138, 142–143
Annulment, of marriage, 129
Appel, Kenneth E., xvii–xix, 3–13
Astley, M. Royden C., 80–96, 220–228, 229–241
Aubrey, Edwin E., 137–145

Bergler, Edmund, 62–63
Bernard, Jessie, 100n
Birth control, 21
church attitudes toward, 140–143, 157 158
Boll, Eleanor Stoker, 107n
Bossard, James H. S., 97–111, 107n, 112, 218
Bowerman, Charles E., 100n
Boys, sex life of, 166–172
Butterfield, Oliver, see Appendix A

Calvin, John, 138
Canada, divorce rate, 97
Capellanus, Andreas, 53–54
Catholic Church, 21
divorce views, 151–154
marriage views, 138, 140, 144, 146–154
sex views, 147–154
Celibacy, 159
Child-parent relations:
adult adjustment and, 40–50, 61–62

family law and, 126–128, 132
family size and, 158
family tensions, 65–74
parents as models, 75–79
Churches, see separate church groups
Clemens, Alphonse H., 146–154, 219n
Clinician, meaning of term, 112
Clinics, marriage counseling, 8
Common-law marriage, 124
Conscience, 33
Contraception, see Birth control
Contract, marriage as, 123–124
Conversation and Communication, Meerloo, 59
Counselor relationship, 229–241
hostility aspects, 237–238
problems in relating, 233–235
rivalry and competitiveness in, 240–241
sexual drives and, 238–239
see also Marriage counseling
Countertransference, 235

Daniels, Anna, see Appendix A
Dependent love, 60–61
Dillon, Thelma, 99
Divorce, 97–111
Catholic Church attitude, 151–154
children in, 110, 132–133
counseling in situations involving, 112–122
as failure, 106–107
grounds for, 128
guilt aspects, 106–107
Jewish attitude, 160
law as applied to, 123–134
occupational aspects, 109
Protestant Church attitudes, 140–141

287